Dedicated to the memory of my father, Albert,
who showed me the joy in gardening,
and my mother, Mary,
who provided the sunshine.

Canadian Cataloguing in Publication Data

Hobson, David

Soiled Reputations

ISBN 0-9682389-0-4

Cover design: **BobCat Graphics**

Cover photo: **Ron Thomson**

Printed and bound in Waterloo, Ontario, Canada
by **1ST IMPRESSION** (519) 885-1090 (recycled paper)

Soiled Reputations

David Hobson

Flip Publishing
Waterloo, Ontario, Canada

Finished at last, with incredible support from
my wife Deb and patient children—
Leighann, Michael, Joel, and Jamie.
Special thanks for the advice, assistance,
friendship, and editing skills of:
April Bulmer, David Corks, Debbie Hobson,
Robert Lyon, Mary Eileen McClear, Pat Dell'Aquila,
Lee Porter, Jill Summerhayes, and the help and
encouragement of all members of the
Cambridge Writer's Collective.
For technical advice, thank you to Paul Psutka.

Thank you all.

An old chinese proverb says:

If you want to be happy for an hour,

get drunk;

If you want to be happy for three days,

get married;

If you want to be happy forever,

make a garden.

That may be, but…

when there's frost in the forecast or the

aphids are hungry,

when there are slugs on the hostas or

blackspot on the roses,

even gardeners need something to smile

about.

— dh

Any resemblance to persons living, dead,
or working in a garden, is purely coincidental.

For more garden humour and news of
<u>Soiled Reputations</u>,
visit: **www.golden.net/~dhobson**

Contents

LABOUR UNREST

What a man needs
in gardening
is a cast iron back
with a hinge in it.

— Charles Dudley Warner

Edgar, my next-door neighbour, passed away suddenly and impressively. He took off to the garden of paradise leaving me with a pile of earthly troubles—and a pile of earth. A pile sitting in his driveway. A pile ordered by me, but delivered to the wrong house. All because Edgar had said "sure" when asked by Backhoe Bill, the illicit soil dealer, if he should dump it. Edgar thought it a gift. This resulted in a tri-lateral dispute of Balkan proportions, all because of a pile of earth; same as any other of the world's disputes, I suppose. Consequently, my pile of soil had lain in Edgar's driveway all winter. Bill wouldn't come back to move it, I refused to, and Edgar, with the tenacity of crab grass, had claimed squatter's rights.

Labour Unrest

With old Edgar gone, the balance of power had shifted, and since the house stood empty there seemed no reason why the soil shouldn't be reclaimed by me, the rightful owner. But I needed help; a truckload of topsoil can destroy a back, and mine was already on the defensive.

I placed an ad in the window of the local variety store—*Boy needed for garden work—good pay!* I hoped it might attract one of the nearby high school kids, a huge one dabbling in steroids and desperate for money. No such luck. I only received two calls, which surprised me considering all the kids I'd seen hanging around the mall with nothing to do.

I arranged the interviews for the following morning. I had it in mind to simply choose the biggest and strongest, but it didn't quite work out that way. First to show up was Erica, a fourteen-year-old feminist. She didn't really want the job; she just came to give me a stinging lecture on the inequality of my hiring practices. By the time she'd finished I felt so guilt-ridden I pleaded with her to take it.

"Please," I begged. "I'll even include lunch."

"Lunch!" she sneered. "You misogynist old fart! You're all the same. You think you can get anything you like for a free lunch. Up yours!" She then made a particularly male gesture before swirling out of the driveway like a dust devil, leaving me flapping in the breeze. I am not an old fart, I said to myself. I may be fifty, but I have the body of a forty nine-year-old.

The next applicant was Mario. He gave a wide berth to Erica as he shuffled toward me mumbling something about needing money for more memory. Then he went into a confusing cybertalk I couldn't understand. From the way he kept blinking at the sunlight I guessed he might be a computer geek. He didn't seem to grasp what I needed, so I tried to communicate digitally by pointing at the pile of soil, then pointing to the backyard. No good. Next I tried using a piece of chalk to draw little wheelbarrow icons on the driveway. Nothing. He continued glancing back and forth from me to the soil.

Finally, I asked in exasperation, "Do you know where potatoes come from?" He looked puzzled. "How about french fries?"

At last his face lit up, "McDonald's?"

I groaned, "Thanks Bill Gates. The information highway begins and ends at a drive-through."

Mario took one last look at me and the topsoil before backing away down the driveway. I gave up and went inside to lie down for a while. I needed to rest. If I didn't find help soon I'd have to move the soil myself.

I'd barely laid down before an insistent hammering on the back door jolted me off the couch. I opened the door. A small, odd-looking boy of around twelve stood there.

"Hello," I said, "what's your name?"

"Gneville."

"Gneville?"

"Yes, Gneville, with a G."

"With a G?"

"You got it. A silent G. You know, G-nu, G-nat, G-nome."

G-neville G-nome, I thought to myself, swallowing a smile—fits. "That's a very interesting name, Gneville. So, you're here to apply for the garden job?"

"No, I came to tell you that for five dollars I'd get rid of the girl who's snapping the heads off your tulips."

"She's what!" I dashed to the front of the house. He was right, someone had broken the heads off my tulips, but there was no one in sight.

"Too late," I said, "she's gone."

"So I guess you owe me five bucks."

"No way. How do I know you didn't break the tulip heads off?"

"You don't, but I can make sure it doesn't happen again."

"Why you little..."

"Okay, okay. Forget it. My Aunt Cyn tells me to always make the most of any opportunity."

"I'm not sure your Aunt had protection rackets in mind. If you need money you'll have to work for it."

"I guess so. I'll take the job instead then. What is it?"

"Moving that topsoil to my backyard. Do you have any experience?"

"Moving topsoil? Sure, I help Backhoe Bill with deliveries."

"That's not exactly shovelling the stuff is it? I'm not certain you're suitable for the position."

"Don't have much choice do you, not if you want to grow anythin' in it this year."

Sharp little bugger, I thought. "What grade are you in Gneville?"

"Twelve, same as my age. I'm advanced. My Mum says my growth spurt went to my head."

I sighed, "I can see it must have. Okay, you can have the job, but stay away from the tulips."

"How much?"

"Well the whole pile of course."

"No, I mean how much will you pay me?"

"What's the least you'll work for?"

"Five dollars an hour and lunch at McDonald's."

"Is that where fries come from?"

"Is this a skill-testing question?"

"Could be."

"No, they come from potatoes, and I can spell it."

"All right," I continued, "Three dollars an hour and a ten dollar gift certificate to McDonald's."

"Four dollars an hour, *and* the gift certificate."

"Four dollars an hour, four hours max, and the gift certificate."

Gneville grinned gnomishly, "Four dollars an hour, four hours max, cash up front, and the gift certificate."

This was beginning to feel like a hostile corporate take-over of my assets, but I needed the soil moved so I agreed. "You have a deal. Eight o'clock tomorrow morning. Don't be late."

The following morning Gneville surprised me by showing up on time.

"Sixteen dollars cash and the certificate," he said bluntly. I paid up and we began filling the wheelbarrow. I'd only tossed three shovels-full in when he announced, "That's enough. I'm not big enough to push it when it's full you know."

"But it'll take forever if we don't fill it."

"Okay, fill it, but then you have to push it."

"Oh, all right."

We compromised by taking turns—full, half full, full, half full. It was a slow process. And while I pushed he sat on the pile whistling the soundtrack from Snow White. I was beginning to dislike Gneville. I tried to get him to reopen the contract but he refused.

"No way," he said. "Four hours is all you paid for, four hours is all you get, and in case you haven't noticed it's five to twelve. Time's up."

"But we've barely moved half the pile you little creep."

"Too bad," he said, waving the gift certificate in my face. "A deal's a deal. I'm going down to McDonald's to pig out—see ya." He reached the end of the driveway and stopped.

“Wait a minute,” he said, squinting at the certificate. “This has expired.”

“Oh really? I hadn't noticed. But then we never discussed validity of the certificate. The large print giveth, and the small print taketh away, kid. Finish moving the soil and I'll take you to McDonald’s, but no pigout.”

“Three Big Macs and a milkshake isn't much. Anyway, how else am I going to grow if I don't eat lots?”

“Have you tried broccoli?”

“Yuck.”

“Push the wheelbarrow and you have a deal.”

“Oh, all right.”

We finished the job and I took Gneville to McDonald’s as promised. I was ravenous. I ate almost as much as he did. I wish I could say we bonded over the burgers, but when he began bragging about the return on his mutual funds, then offering to flip a coin for a fourth burger, I refused. I had an uneasy feeling I'd be meeting him again—after he'd evolved into my bank manager. I didn't have to wait that long…

SOILED REPUTATIONS

Who loves a garden
still his Eden keeps,
perennial pleasures plants,
and wholesome harvests keeps.

— Amos Bronson Alcott

I no sooner had the topsoil in my possession than a '**For Sale**' sign went up next door and real estate agents began arriving daily with potential buyers. I made a point of puttering around the yard, curious to see who my new neighbours might be. Anyone had to be an improvement over Edgar.

Meanwhile, with the extra soil, I began to enlarge my flowerbeds, which meant I needed more plants. In Edgar's backyard grew one or two rare perennials he'd insisted were family heirlooms. He'd refused to give me a cutting, not even a seedpod. Now, with the house in limbo, and by convincing myself the new owners wouldn't appreciate Edgar's hard work, I felt I could take advantage of the opportunity to enrich my yard at no one's expense.

It had been quiet when I'd pushed my wheelbarrow cautiously up the driveway and into the backyard, where I began digging out a few plants to complement my landscaping. Unfortunately, I got a little carried away. Unfortunate, because unbeknownst to me the house had been sold, and the new owner surprised me by showing up just as I was struggling to get a huge clump of rare Coreopsis into the wheelbarrow.

"Drop that shovel you perennial pilferer!" The imperious voice from the back porch startled me. I jerked upright, almost putting my back out.

"That's a little unfair," I said, "I don't make a habit of this." The owner of the voice strode aggressively toward me, a tall, strong-looking woman wearing yellow rubber boots. With her frightening red hair and flashing green eyes she was a manic traffic signal.

"What exactly do you think you're doing?" she hollered. "This is my property. I bought the place because I fell in love with the garden, and here I find some creep ripping out the flowerbeds."

I had to think quickly. She sounded like Erica—only bigger.

"Well, er, I er." I mumbled, "I'm er. I'm just carrying out old Edgar's last wishes. He died here, you know. I mean he lived here. That is, he lived here, then he died here, right on this very spot—really."

"He did?" she gasped. "How?"

"Doing what he loved most. Driving his garden

tractor around and around the yard." (And driving the neighbours crazy, I said to myself). "He must have fallen off the tractor, because it was still running when I found him."

"Oh, how awful."

"I'll say. Those suckers have a huge gas tank. Anyway, I arrived on the scene first, just in time to hear his dying wishes. He asked me to care for these plants, to provide them with a loving home, to nurture them as though they were his children."

"Oh the poor man," she said, her voice softening. By the time I'd finished she had tears in her eyes. She begged me to take the remaining plants. "He must have been a wonderful gardener. I couldn't live here knowing a dear old man's last wishes hadn't been fulfilled. Please let me help. By the way, my name is Cynthia."

"Pleasure to meet you," I said. "Just call me Riley."

Her assistance was a bonus, because I'd spotted a few more plants I could use. She helped me dig them out and she even pushed the wheelbarrow. She was really strong, and very attractive. Definitely an improvement over Edgar. As we worked we chatted pleasantly, gently probing each other's background.

"And so, Mr. Riley," she asked, "what kind of business are you in?"

"Well, none really. I guess you could say I'm semi-retired. I used to work for the municipality; now I have a part-time job with the library."

"Oh, so you're a literary type."

"Hmm—yes, I suppose I am. I do collect a lot of books."

"You mean rare ones?"

"Kind of. I'm actually a bounty hunter for the library, but I don't like to brag about it. Too many people have overdue books in their closets."

"How interesting. Well, it's obvious you still find time for your garden. It's very nice and—er, lush."

This was true. Where Edgar's—now Cynthia's—backyard would be described as immaculate, a miniature Versailles; mine would be charitably described as abstract, in the English cottage garden style. Edgar hated it. He enjoyed conformity; I preferred variety, in rampant abundance. Edgar followed the reform and restrict school; I favoured benign tolerance—toward plants, not always toward Edgar. This often led to some rancorous disagreements over garden policy. Fortunately, a sturdy fence separated our yards, preventing serious injury. At least Cynthia looked like a neighbour who *might* be easier to get along with.

She continued, "And I can see the hard work has kept you in shape."

"Why, thank you. And what about you, Cynthia. What do you do?"

"You won't believe this, Mr. Riley, but I'm also in the

literary field. I'm a sportswriter."

"A sportswriter? That must be exciting. But isn't it—well—you know...."

"Go on, say it."

"Say what?" I said, backing away a little.

"You know very well. A *man's* occupation? I've heard it often enough."

"No, not at all. I think it's a wonderful job for a woman. I just thought you appeared far too smart and attractive to be hanging around locker rooms. That's no place for a talented writer."

She smiled. "You are so right."

Phew, I thought, you've still got it Riley.

"I've had enough of smelly men and smelly women," she went on. "I'm getting out of it, going freelance, maybe do some garden writing.

"Oh, you know a lot about gardening do you?"

"No, absolutely nothing," she laughed, then whispered. "Don't tell anyone, but I know nothing about sports either. I just churn out statistics with lots of clichés and bad puns thrown in. It's easy. Gardening should be a cinch too, and definitely more fragrant. I'm sure I'll soon pick up all I need to know; all the raw material is right here."

"Well, most of it," I muttered.

"What did you say?"

"I said you can count on me to help," I replied, ingratiating myself tastefully. "You only have to ask."

"Thank you. That's very kind of you. I can see we're going to make wonderful neighbours."

Cynthia really took to gardening, amazing me with her enthusiasm. She read everything on the subject and worked hard at maintaining Edgar's high standards, even making improvements—except for one thing. Right in the front yard she placed a huge, ugly, garden gnome. It blended in like a clown at a funeral. As she was a new neighbour I didn't say anything to her. When she asked, I said, "It's lovely; I've always wanted one myself," and left it at that. I didn't want to upset her; one dose of her displeasure was enough. We gradually became regular gardening buddies, helping each other out when the need arose. I even felt a little guilty about leaving her yard looking like a garden centre after final clearance, so I offered her a few things I had extras of, like violets and lily of the valley. I gave her all I could dig out.

Sadly, our blossoming friendship lasted about as long as a day lily in December. I was relaxing on the front steps one mild spring morning, with a coffee in hand, watching Cynthia learn the difference between weeds and groundcover, when Backhoe Bill showed up with a truckload of topsoil she'd ordered. He backed up the truck in her driveway, but refused to dump the load unless she paid up immediately—in cash.

"Not very trusting, is he?" Cynthia said.

"I wonder why," I mumbled, trying to duck out of

sight of Bill, hoping he wouldn't recognise me.
He didn't, but Gneville did. He was riding shotgun on Bill's dump truck. Worse still, Cynthia was *Aunt Cyn.*

"Hi, Aunt Cyn, I didn't know you lived here."

"What do you mean," Cynthia frowned. "Didn't your mum tell you?"

"She's been away. She won the jackpot at bingo, then caught a bus to Las Vegas before her luck ran out. She just got back last week. I guess she forgot. I bet you're glad me and Mr. Riley moved the pile of topsoil for you. Hey, Bill, this is the house where I moved all the topsoil. Remember, where you said the guy should be planted in it for taking advantage of kids."

Bill is big, a fast eater and a slow talker. He's driven truck so long he has Popeye forearms. They say he can crush a rutabaga in one hand.

"So," he snarled, leaning from the cab, "it's you, runty Riley. You got your topsoil. I get my cash, right? Or we start planting."

"Wait a minute," Cynthia interrupted. "What topsoil are we talking about?"

"The pile I dumped here last fall," Bill answered, "just before old Edgar kicked off. It sat here all winter."

"Last fall?" Cynthia said. She turned to me with a puzzled look. "I bought the house, the lot, and the contents, including topsoil, but I don't recall seeing any. Did you see any topsoil, Riley? You couldn't miss it.

It would look a lot like this load—if there was one."

As I tried to explain, her face began to change colour like a time-lapse film of a tomato ripening.

"You creep! I can't imagine why a nice old guy like Edgar would ask anything of a wretch like you. Least of all with his dying words."

"Dying words?" Bill snorted. "Old Edgar didn't have any dying words, at least none that're repeatable."

"Oh, and why was that?" Cynthia asked.

"Didn't have time," Bill grinned. "He'd got out of his car at the lion safari, see, to collect elephant droppings for his roses. They say it's the best thing for growing jumbo buds."

"Then what?" demanded Cynthia, impatiently.

"Well, I guess he got a bit too eager. Fat Alex, the big bull, he didn't like the personal attention, so he backed up—a little too quickly for old Edgar. Like I said, no time for last words."

"Let me get this straight, runty Riley. If Edgar didn't pass away in his own backyard, you didn't hear any last words. Therefore, he didn't bequeath anything to anyone, not plants, not top soil, not anything. Right?"

"Right," I sighed.

"And if the pile of topsoil had remained here as part of the house and contents, which I purchased, I wouldn't have had to order this load. Right?"

"Right—I mean wrong"

"What do you mean, *wrong?*"

"I mean it was my topsoil. I ordered it."

"But you didn't pay for it," Bill roared from his cab.

"That's right," Cynthia said. "but this one's going to cost you. So, pay the gentleman, runty Riley, so he can dump *my* load. Then I might suggest you return all the perennials to me, the rightful owner. You may, if you wish, wait until suitable transplanting weather." She then handed me a shovel and screamed in my face, "Topsoil! Twenty four hours, buster. Start digging. And while you're at it, you can take your crummy violets back."

"Want some help, Mr. Riley?" squawked Gneville. "We can make a deal."

"He don't need any help," Bill growled. "Anyway, it must be lunchtime, Gneville. Let's see if the truck'll fit in the new drive-through at McDonald's.

I spent the rest of the day cursing Edgar as I moved Cynthia's topsoil into her backyard. She sat on the deck, watching. At three o'clock she asked me sweetly if I'd like a glass of water, and then ignored me until I'd dumped the final load at six o'clock.

"Hungry, Riley?"

"What do you think?"

"Tell you what. Buy supper and your debt is paid."

"McDonald's?" I said, hopefully. I'd already spent enough on this woman.

"McDonald's? Come on, Riley. What do you want, peace, or stepped up border patrols? Take me for a decent meal and I may even consider forgiving you, although I'm sure old Edgar won't."

"Who cares. If there's any justice he'll be stuck in Paradise with a push mower."

PUMPKIN PASSION

Little garden gods,
Bless the time of sowing,
Watering and growing;
Bless our garden that it may…
Beat our nextdoor neighbour's.

— Patrick Reginald Chalmers

"Good morning, Riley. Isn't it a beautiful day?"

"Oh, good morning," I called to the voice coming from the other side of the fence. It was Cynthia. I was busy preparing my vegetable garden for planting, but I paused to chat.

"Lovely weather, Cynthia, just lovely. I see spring cleanup is going well; your compost heap is getting quite high. I'll give you a hand to turn it if you like."

"Why, thank you, Riley. That's very kind of you."

I was eager to appear friendly and helpful, hoping to perhaps repair my soiled reputation. The past week or two we'd been exchanging the occasional pleasantry over the fence. It looked as though a neighbourly friendship might still blossom despite our earlier misunderstanding. It helped too that we were both experiencing the joy any gardener feels when working the soil again after a long miserable winter. Dirt under the fingernails seems to act as a placebo on lingering animosities.

"So," Cynthia said cheerily, "what vegetables are you planting this year?"

"Oh, asparagus, broccoli, carrots."

"Really? Do you always grow things alphabetically?"

"Huh? Oh, I get it. Ha ha, very funny. No, I just enjoy eating them. And, of course, I'll be growing pumpkins."

"Pumpkins? How many pumpkins can you eat?"

"I don't eat them, at least not these, they're competition pumpkins."

"Competition pumpkins? I would never have guessed you were the competitive type, Riley. Then again, it does seem everything in your yard is competing. Do you ever prune anything?"

"I happen to appreciate luxuriant growth. And if you must know I can be a formidable competitor, especially in the face of an injustice; which is exactly what I suffered over the years at the hand of Edgar. He always won the Horticultural Society's pumpkin growing contest, *every* year. I came second, *every* year. I swear he cheated somehow but I could never prove it."

"Now, Riley, it's not very nice to speak ill of the dead."

"You didn't know Edgar. He took extreme pleasure in seeing me fail. I used to love pumpkin pie, but the psychological effect of losing so often ruined my taste for it. I'm sure winning would bring it back."

"Well, just to be neighbourly, I'll bake you a pie if you win."

"Wow! No one's ever made me a home-baked pie before. That's terrific."

I was really excited, until she added, "In fact I might just enter myself, although I don't know much about growing pumpkins, then if I win you can bake *me* one."

"Sounds fair I suppose, but I doubt you'll have much chance of winning. It takes years of experience to grow giant pumpkins, and you need the right seeds."

"You do?"

"Oh yes, you can't use just any old seeds. They have to be one of the giant hybrids. I've spent the winter researching pumpkins and perusing catalogues. I'm growing *Supernova*, forecast to be the first thousand pounder."

"Just a sec." Cynthia disappeared into the house. She returned moments later with an old mason jar.

"What are these? I found them in the fruit cellar. They look like pumpkin seeds, and it says something about Leviathan on the lid." My heart sank as she continued breezily, "They must have been left behind when the house was cleared out. Wouldn't it be something if they were Edgar's prize-winning seeds? I bet they are. It's as though they're his legacy. I can't wait to plant them."

"Oh, well, go ahead I suppose, but they're probably old ones. If you like I'll test them, you know, to see if they're still viable."

"Not a chance, Riley. If these are prize-winning seeds you'd be the last person I'd give them to. You're not getting your hands on these babies. I hope you bake good pie because I aim to continue the tradition and win this contest. I'll do old Edgar proud, just you wait and see."

I could taste pumpkin pie in my mouth and it didn't taste good. If Cynthia had Edgar's prize seeds, I wouldn't stand a chance. I felt like conceding, not even planting pumpkins, but as she walked away she called over her shoulder, "I'm going to plant them right now."

"Yes," I breathed with relief, then shouted, "Great idea, plant them all, but don't stand too close. They grow so fast you might get trapped against the fence."

"Why thank you, Riley. That's the spirit. I'd hate to have a little friendly competition spoil our new friendship. Good luck to you too."

I smiled to myself as I returned to digging. I was

still in the running because Cynthia was making a big mistake. It was only the 5th of May and she was rushing off to start planting, when any fool would know it was way too early for pumpkins. I had mine growing indoors. They'd be ready for planting out as soon as the weather warmed up enough.

In the meantime, I kept an eye on her pumpkin patch; it was on the other side of the fence, right next to where I planned mine. Amazingly, her seeds actually germinated, and thanks to May being unusually warm they were off to a good start. Good enough to worry me.

I began watching the weather forecast every night on TV, hoping the jet stream would swoop down with a vicious frost, but it was stuck over Kapuskasing. In spite of his predictions, Whacky Willby, the TV weatherman, was acting the hero as usual, taking full credit for the balmy weather. It upset me so much I wrote him a nasty letter in which I asked how he could get things consistently wrong and still keep his job. He didn't reply.

At the end of May I transplanted my seedlings to the nice sunny location I'd prepared, where I continued to nurture them. I mulched them with compost and fertilized often. One morning I accidentally gave Cynthia's plants a squirt of fertilizer when a gust of wind carried some over the fence.

Oh well, I thought, they can never get too much.

The problem was, they did, because she fertilized again that evening before I had chance to warn her. The damage was done. I didn't dare admit I'd been careless.

"Oh no," she said, as she gazed at her wilted seedlings.

"That's too bad, Cynthia. Must have been a late frost. Doesn't seem to have caught mine though."

"It wouldn't would it" she snapped back.

"Wait a minute. I hope you're not suggesting I had anything to do with *your* failure. What do you think I am?"

She glared, and said sarcastically, "Do you want the book or the video?"

Our friendship was wilting again. Disappointing I suppose, but I cheered up at the thought I now had less competition, or so I believed.

I glanced into Cynthia's yard a few days later, only to see her plants flourishing, healthier than ever.

"And what do you think you're doing, Riley?"
I looked up to see her approaching.

"Just looking."

"That had better be all you're doing."

"But—but they were dying. What happened? Did they recover?"

"Course not. I had a few seedlings in reserve, growing in pots on the Patio—Edgar's idea."

"What do you mean *Edgar's* idea?"

"You won't believe this, but when I searched through the fruit cellar, I found his old garden journal. It has complete instructions for growing everything, including pumpkins. Too bad, Riley, come fall the only pie you'll be eating will be crow." I stomped away to the house in search of a Rolaid; my stomach already aching.

Throughout the summer Cynthia and I were polite but cool toward each other as we cared diligently for our pumpkins, feeding, weeding, and watering.
By August they were in superb condition. I began to worry again; I'd done everything I could to boost the growth of mine, but they seemed no bigger than hers were. I decided to do some culling, get rid of the runts. I was hacking away when Cynthia startled me.

"Quitting are you?"

"No I'm not," I replied testily, "I'm just removing the weak ones. This ensures all the riches of the ground will be channelled to the prime pumpkin, something like Ronald Reagan's trickle down theory, or trickle up in this case."

"I think it was trickle up in Reagan's case too. What a great idea. Edgar's instructions didn't mention that. Kind of you to tell me."

I swore to myself. Me and my big mouth. She set to work culling hers immediately. An hour later we each had just one good-sized pumpkin left, and it was impossible to say which was the larger. From then on they grew rapidly. By September they were a pair of rival body builders bulking up for the big show. I even began calling mine Schwartzeneger, hoping it might psyche Cynthia's out. It didn't help. The contest date loomed, and I still couldn't tell which was the larger.

I simply had to know. So after dark on the next cloudy night I dressed in black clothing, donned a ski mask, and slipped quietly over the fence. With my flashlight and tape measure I crept toward the pumpkin. I'd barely moved a couple of feet when the whole backyard lit up like a prison break. Floodlights! I was silhouetted against the fence with an image of James Cagney in *White Heat* flashing through my head. I even heard gunfire, but it was only static from the megaphone Cynthia was using to bark orders at me.

"Get out of my yard you dirty rat," she bellowed. I went over the fence like a guilty cat.

"I only wanted to measure it," I shouted back.

"Measure it!" she bellowed again, loud enough to wake the whole neighbourhood, "I've got your measure, Riley, and it's short, so take off!"

I stayed a safe distance from Cynthia's yard for a few days, until my curiosity got the better of me. While hoeing a few weeds one afternoon, I casually worked my way close enough to glance into her yard. I stared in dismay. Her pumpkin, identical to mine, was now totally enclosed by chicken wire. I heard her screen door slam, so I scrunched down behind the fence.

"You can show your face," she called out, "I know you're there, I have the yard under surveillance."
I poked my head up to see her marching down the path, followed by her gnomic nephew.

"Gneville's going to keep an eye on my pumpkins, make sure no vermin gets near them. I've promised to take him to Disneyworld if I win the contest."

"They'll probably want to keep him," I muttered, then sneered, "Go ahead, I doubt if chicken wire will keep anything out."

"It will when the power's on," Cynthia smiled, rolling out an extension cord. "Plug it in, Gneville."

"Too bad we don't have something live to test it on, Aunt Cyn." He had his beady little Gnome eyes on me as he said this. I was determined to win now more than ever. I'd already lost enough sleep over this competition. Depriving the little rodent of a trip to Florida would be a bonus, something to make the stress of competition worthwhile.

I still desperately needed to know whose pumpkin was the healthier, so after they'd left I heaved myself up onto the fence. With a long bamboo cane I gave her pumpkin a little prod, to see if it was as solid as mine was, but as I reached out I lost my balance. I was so terrified of plunging over and getting electrocuted that I used the cane to support myself. Cynthia's pumpkin may have been solid, but my weight was too much for it. The cane harpooned its way right into the heart of it. I managed to regain my balance and quickly withdrew the cane. It came out with a horrible slurping plop, leaving a neat hole the size of a slug from a forty-five. Although I hadn't intended any harm, I felt guilty. It had been an accident, and I should have confessed, but I knew Cynthia would never believe me. There was nothing I could do now; her pumpkin was doomed. Winning was obviously my destiny. If the real slugs didn't get in the beetles would, and they did. From that day on her pumpkin shrivelled and shrank till it looked like a large orange prune. Meanwhile, mine grew massive. It looked like the sun rising in my backyard. Cynthia couldn't figure out what had gone wrong. I offered my condolences, but she refused to speak, clearly suspecting me. I didn't care though, success was in sight. When Gneville appeared, I whistled, *Hi Ho Hi Ho*, and called out, "Your pumpkin's looking a little—*Mickey Mouse*, isn't it Gneville?"

For the rest of summer and fall I practically set up camp in the yard, guarding my pumpkin. Nothing was going to deprive me of victory. I had good reason to be confident; word around the garden centre had me a clear winner. As measuring day approached I could taste pie. It was good.

October 1st arrived, a gorgeous sunny day. The media showed up early, including TV, and a photographer from '*Roots and Fruits*'. I wasn't too impressed with the way they trampled everything in the yard, but I was happy. It was my day in the sun. I even waved to Cynthia as she stood on the back porch glaring. More than her thumb was green.

The TV director called for everyone to stand clear as measuring took place. He must have been searching for some way to illustrate the size of the monster, because he asked one of the crew to pick up a kid and sit him on top of my pumpkin.

"*Gneville*," I swore to myself. He must have slipped into my yard with the crowd. He didn't hesitate to stand up on the pumpkin and dance around. I wanted to strangle the little bugger, but it wouldn't look good on the evening news, so I moved in close. Then, just at the moment of announcement, as the cameras began to roll, I gave the pumpkin a shove, rocking it slightly. Gneville slid off and disappeared from sight, just as the president of the Horticulture Society, a Mr. Gradely, began to speak.

"I am proud to announce the winner of this year's *Giant Pumpkin Contest* is... A muffled voice from behind the pumpkin called out:

"My Aunt Cyn! Look! Right here." Everyone strained to see. "This pumpkin's stalk goes right under the fence; it grew from my Aunt's yard.

"By golly, the lad's right," said Mr. Gradely as Gneville emerged. "It has grown from under the fence."

Gneville clambered back on top and whooped at the top of his voice, "My Aunt Cyn's the contest winner, and I'm going to Disneyworld."

Cynthia came running.

"What do you mean, Gneville?" she asked breathlessly. "My pumpkin shrivelled up a month ago. I can't have won."

The contest chairman explained the situation.

"*All right!*" she said, sneering at me.

"But—but it's in my yard," I pleaded. "If it's in my yard, then surely I must be the winner."

"It was nourished from *my* yard," Cynthia interrupted. "I reared it from seed."

"And who's been taking care of it? This side of the fence gets more sun. It couldn't have grown this big on your side. Nothing would grow in your yard if it wasn't for Edgar."

"Why you..." Cynthia dropped her gardening gloves and started toward me. I stepped behind Mr. Gradely.

"Calm down," he said, "calm down. It seems to me a compromise would be in order here."

"No way!" Cynthia and I said together. "It's all or nothing. There can be only *one* winner."

"Well then," Mr. Gradely said, "If you can't

compromise, are you willing to let the celebrity judge decide?"

"You bet." I said, "He's sure to see my point."

"Yes," said Cynthia, "let him settle it. It's obvious whose pumpkin it is anyway."

An announcement was made, and the celebrity judge summoned. Mr. Gradely introduced him to Cynthia and me, a Mr. Willby. He looked very familiar.

"Don't I know you?" I said pleasantly, hoping to gain his favour.

"Oh I'm sure you do," he smiled, "because I certainly know you."

"Wait a minute—don't tell me. It'll come to me."

"I'll give you a clue," he said, smiling, "*Thanks to the jet stream there's a cold front moving into your neighbourhood. It will be followed by an intense depression bringing heavy cloud for the next few weeks.* How's that, Mr. Riley of 37 Havelock Crescent. Remember me now?" The temperature fell rapidly. "Better luck next year, Mr. Riley. And to you, Ms. Cynthia…, may I offer my sincerest congratulations. Wherever you plan to celebrate, I'm sure the weather will be sunny and warm."

"Great! Keep an eye on the yard will you, Riley. Gneville and I are off to Florida. You're welcome to keep the pumpkin. You may even be able to salvage enough for a pie before it rots."

CRIMINAL GARDENERS

Where are the dear, old-fashioned posies,
Quaint in form and bright in hue,
Such as grandma gave her lovers
When she walked the garden through?
— Ethel Lynn Beers

For gardeners, the longest, darkest days of winter are during the miserable months of November and December. Fall colour is forgotten, spring renewal a foggy dream. Apt sentiments printed on my garden calendar. It was no different for me and Cynthia, except with the pumpkins rotting on the compost heap, the hostility level had sunk to its lowest. Throw in the goodwill of the Christmas season and by January we were communicating like strangers in an elevator.

As we were shovelling snow one evening, a bond slowly began to form as we cursed the snowplough that plugged our driveways.

"Tell me, Cynthia," I said, heaving on another shovel-full. "Why is it the snowplough always dumps more snow in my driveway than it does in yours?"

"Haven't you figured that out yet?"

"No I haven't. I don't understand, enlighten me."

"Next time the plough comes down the street, check out the driver a little more closely. Look, here he comes now."

"It can't be. It is. It's Backhoe Bill plugging my driveway. Why would he keep doing that? I paid him for the topsoil long ago."

"I don't know. He's always very nice to me. He offered to bring me a free load of soil next spring."

"Oh really. What did you do. Offer to bake him a pie or something?"

"No, I didn't. I only bake pies for people I like. As for the soil, forget it. If I've got something Bill wants to buy; he can't afford it. No, I imagine he's bored and gets his kicks playing king of the snow banks. Think of the power. I wouldn't mind having the job myself."

"*Cynthia!* You mean you'd plough people in on purpose?"

"Course not. Well, maybe a few, you know, like telemarketers, politicians, sexist pigs, soil thieves. Oh yes, and drug-dealers; I'd really like to plough them in. What about you Riley? Wouldn't you like to plough someone in?"

"Well, now I think about it, yes. Whacky Willby the weatherman for sure, people who write in library books, all those jerks that park in places reserved for the handicapped. I'd *really* plough them in. And tailgaters especially; they drive me nuts."

"Right on, Riley. And what about people who don't return shopping carts?"

"Yeah! I'd also like to plough in that special person who's always ahead of me in line at the coffee shop. Right when I'm desperate for a coffee, they always have to ask for a toasted bagel. That timer on the toaster is like a ticking bomb."

"I like toasted bagels."

"Then you'd better not get ahead of me in the coffee shop. One of these days, I tell you..."

"My goodness, you're a real tyrant. Tell you what. Forget the coffee. I think we deserve some hot chocolate. I'll go make us some while you finish up my driveway."

"What do you mean finish it up? You're only half done. How be I make the hot chocolate and you finish *my* driveway?"

"Because it was my idea, and anyway, I doubt the health department would approve of you serving foodstuffs."

I choked down an opinion. Cynthia was being unusually pleasant to me, and hot chocolate sounded great, so I shovelled her driveway. By the time I'd finished I was practically on my knees crawling to her front door. I managed to ring the doorbell. No answer.

I rang again, and again. Finally the door opened.

"Hot chocolate," I gasped.

"Hot chocolate? Oh yes, I almost forgot, I was about to take a shower and go to bed. I thought you were finished ages ago."

"What?"

"Just kidding. Pull out those old lawn chairs, Riley. We'll sit here on the porch."

"What's wrong with the kitchen? I am house trained you know."

"Maybe, maybe not, but my hot chocolate is best drunk outside."

I took a sip. "Wow! I can see why. Drunk is right. What did you put in it?"

"Never mind. It's my secret. Now, wasn't it worth shovelling the rest of the driveway?"

"I'll say. Speaking of secrets, I notice you've been parking your car outside lately. Why aren't you using your garage?"

"I am using it, but not for the car. Oh, come on. Since you're so curious, I'll show you. I wouldn't want you to be caught snooping around and be arrested as a peeping Tom."

"Cynthia, I'm shocked. That's the kindest thing you've ever said to me. Any more hot chocolate and I'll start to fantasize."

"In your dreams, Riley. I can see I made it a little too strong for you. Let's go before I change my mind."

She led the way into the garage, pointing out the rat proof lock as she called it. I couldn't help but sense a note of lingering reproach in her voice. She flicked on the light. I was amazed. The garage had been insulated, heated, and painted a brilliant white.

"You've been busy."

"Hydroponics," she said proudly. "This way I'll be able to grow things all year long. I've fallen in love with gardening and everything that goes with it."

"Backhoe Bill goes with gardening y'know."

"Okay, I love gardening and everything that goes with it, except for Backhoe Bill."

"That's better."

"Riley! If I didn't know you were a perfectly contented, middle-aged bachelor in love with himself, his garden, and his pick-up truck, I'd say you were a tiny bit jealous of Bill."

"I confess, Cynthia. I am."

"You are?"

"Yes, he has a bigger truck."

"And he drives better too."

"Ouch!"

"Speaking of pick-ups. How be we use that pile of scrap you own to go fetch my lighting equipment?"

"Thanks a lot, Cynthia. I'm not one to say, *What's in it for me?* But, what's in it for me? Apart from more hot chocolate."

"Well, if you're really helpful I'll let you have a corner

to grow your own stuff."

"You will? That would be great! Sure I'll help. My windowsills get so crowded it's impossible to see outside by spring.

Next day we took the truck and drove out to the industrial basin where we spent half an hour searching for the store because Cynthia had forgotten the instructions. We found it finally, hidden behind an abandoned truck stop. Despite its obscurity the parking lot was packed.

"This place has the ambience of a pool hall on pay-day," I whispered to Cynthia as we entered.

"You're not kidding."

"Are you sure this is the right place? These guys all look like rock band roadies or retired Hell's Angels. And by the look of all the dogs they have with them they're pet lovers too. If you can call them pets. Any one of them looks as though it could rip the hide off an alligator."

"Be quiet, Riley. Of course it's the right place. Just load the truck and let's get out of here."

Cynthia's equipment was all packed up ready for her. She paid the bill, which was substantial, then we lugged the boxes out to the truck. We were about to drive off when Earl, the storeowner, called us back in.

"I almost forgot, Miss Cynthia, since you purchased the #1 Gold package, set up is included. Mace and Juice will be over tonight to help you with it."

He gestured to a couple of bystanders that looked far from innocent. The one called Mace looked like four hundred pounds of fast food brought to a sudden standstill. He had a shaven head and tattooed knuckles, and was wearing a tee shirt which read—*Pitbulls R Us*. His littermate, Juice, was as skinny and wasted as resurrected roadkill, with the teeth removed.

"Are you sure you know who you're dealing with?" I asked. At the mention of dealing, the room went quiet. I was about to suggest we go home quickly and lock ourselves in, when the silence was broken by the sound of a Harley low on oil. It was Mace speaking.

"We've got the address," he growled. We'll be over around ten. Should be finished by three, including the planting."

"What planting?" Cynthia asked.

"Oh, we always start our customers out right," Earl smiled. "I like the first crop to be successful, that way you'll be hooked. Is there anything in particular you'd like to try?"

"Well I've always dreamed of growing delphiniums," Cynthia replied.

"Perfect, we have some seedlings you'll just love, a new hybrid—Hawaiian Surprise. Take about a dozen to get her started, Juice."

"Sure will. Schee you later, Missh Schinthia," Juice said, with a toothless smile.

We drove home in silence. Cynthia seemed

unconcerned, but I had the feeling she'd just bought a lifetime membership in a 'Plant of the Month Club'. We returned to her place where I helped unload everything and carry it into the garage, then quickly said a cheery, "Bye, Cynthia, see you tomorrow."

"What do you mean tomorrow? You'd better be here this evening if you want any growing space. Gneville is coming around to help, he'll probably want to show you his new vermi-composter." She gestured to a large blue container in the back corner of the garage.

"I can hardly wait. All right, I'll be here."

At eight o'clock I returned to find Cynthia busy trying to screw in a huge lamp bulb, while Gneville appeared to be climbing into the blue container.
I resisted the urge to give him a gentle nudge.

"How are the *verms,* Gneville?" I asked. I wish I hadn't. He stood up quickly, sticking out his hand. I can face a worm or two, but having a handful pushed under my nose is the not the kind of intimate response I was looking for. A formal introduction would have been quite sufficient.

"Lovely aren't they, Mr. Riley? Would you like to help feed 'em? They'll eat just about anything—and fast." I reconsidered the nudge, but said instead, "No thanks, Gneville. As a fast-food fanatic, I'm sure you're well qualified to understand their diet. He muttered something I didn't catch because we were interrupted by the sound of a motorcycle outside.

The garage door shook, then burst open, and in roared Mace and Juice. Why they would be riding a motorcycle in January only the frozen chosen would understand.

Mace shut down the Harley and growled, "Right on time, Miss Cynthia. Here's the number."

"What number?" Cynthia asked.

"Caligula's Pizza," Mace grunted, "Just order a few large with lots of anchovies. Just anchovies." The mention of food must have over-stimulated Juice because he began to drool.

"Nishe plashce," he said. "Should be able manage a nishe operation here."

They both got to work immediately, setting up the stands, wiring and attaching the bulbs, installing water tubing. Despite appearances these guys were real experts. I was impressed. By three a.m. the garage had begun to resemble a small laboratory, with plants. Cynthia was beaming.

"And these are my delphiniums?" she asked, picking up a tray of seedlings.

"Sure are, Mish Schinshia," Juice replied.

"An' you don't need to worry about 'em at all," Mace added. "Everythin' is automatic. You can ignore 'em if you like. We'll pop by once a week or so just to check up on 'em. We want these to be a real success for you." They then packed up their leftover pizzas and roared off into the night.

Mace and Juice were true to their word; every week or so they came by to check on the seedlings, top up the water containers, and generally give advice, often on the best toppings for pizza.

By the beginning of March the garage was a rainforest. All the plants and seedlings were thriving, especially Cynthia's delphiniums. Mind you, they were the strangest delphiniums I'd ever seen. When I suggested this to Cynthia she accused me of jealousy and made veiled threats against my petunias. From then on I kept my opinions to myself.

A couple of days later I was out shovelling a late snowfall from my driveway when I heard a cry of anguish from the garage. I made the mistake of poking my head in. Cynthia had a pair of garden shears in her hand and a murderous look in her eyes.

"Where are they, Riley?" she demanded.

"Where are what?" I asked, although it was clear what she referred to. Her prized delphiniums were gone. Snipped off at the base, not a leaf remained.

"That's odd," I said, "Who'd want 'em when they weren't even blooming. What possible use could they be to anyone?"

We soon received the answer to this with the arrival of Mace and Juice.

"Too bad about the first crop, Ms. Cynthia," Mace said, "they were developing Delphinium Droop. We had to execute emergency measures before the whole garage got infected. We executed 'em, but don't worry; we have another batch c' young plants. They'll catch up in no time, and still be ready for spring planting."

"Oh thank you guys, you're so kind," Cynthia said. "Aren't they wonderful, Riley? It's so nice to have people you can count on."

"Sure is," I agreed. I couldn't conceive of not agreeing, not after Mace turned as he was leaving and said casually, "Oh, and by the way, I swear that truck out there was tailgating me on the Expressway this morning. If you happen to see the owner, tell him Mace gets really pissed off at tailgaters."

"Isn't that nice," Cynthia said after they'd left, "You and Mace have something in common, Riley."

"So do you, Cynthia. You both seem awfully fond of those delphiniums. I can't wait to see them flower."

It was only after I noticed the same car parked across the street three days in a row that I really began to worry. Someone was watching the garage. I went over to speak to Cynthia about it. Gneville was there feeding his worms. I'd just begun to explain when someone hammering on the garage door interrupted us.

"Police, open up—now." It didn't sound like they'd ask twice. Cynthia was speechless. I already had visions of attack dogs and tear gas in my head, so immediately I rushed to obey.

"Don't open it," Gneville said. "Ask him if he has a warrant," Gneville was clearly a graduate of Saturday morning cartoon crime school.

"Got a warrant—sir?" I asked.

"No, but if you insist we'll be back in half an hour with one. Don't think of leaving. We then heard a large vehicle backing up into the driveway.

"You won't believe this," I said, peeping through a crack in the door. "They're ploughing us in."

"What do you mean *ploughing* us in?"

"They're using a snowplough to block the door, and Bill is driving it. You *should* have baked him a pie, Cynthia. We're trapped!"

"What on earth is going on?" she asked.

"I bet they came for the marijuana," Gneville said.

"What marijuana?"

"Over there, the plants marked delphiniums. You didn't think you could fool anyone did you?"

"Why didn't you tell me?" Cynthia yelled.

"I thought you knew," squirmed Gneville, "you're a member of the Gro-Do Coop aren't you?"

"The Gro-Do Coop? What Gro-Do Coop? What the heck have we got involved in? We're all going to have criminal records."

"If only we could get rid of the evidence," I said.

"How? We can't get out of the garage."

"Easy," said Gneville, "feed it to my worms."

"Feed it to your worms? Gneville, you're brilliant," Cynthia said, hugging him. For once I had to agree.

"I hope they're hungry," I said as we uprooted the

'delphiniums' and frantically stuffed them into the vermi-composter.

"Starving," Gneville grinned.

We'd only just shoved the last stalks into the box when the drug squad returned with their warrant. They searched the garage completely, finding nothing but flowers and vegetables. They were about to leave when one of the officers noticed the vermi-composter. Gneville was sitting on it.

"What's in the box, kid?"

"Worms. Look for yourself," Gneville said. A little over confidently I thought. The cop wrenched the lid off, then recoiled in disgust at the sight of hundreds of worms lying prostrate on the surface of the compost.

"Looks like you opened a can of worms there officer," I smirked, foolishly, because his hand jerked toward his holster and his eye began to twitch.
I almost swallowed my Adam's apple. Luckily for me Gneville was right about the worms being hungry; not a leaf remained in the box. Boy, was the cop mad.

He glared at me and snarled, "Next time..." Then after giving a grudging apology they all jumped into their cruisers and roared off.

"Enjoy your donut," Gneville yelled after them.

"Speaking of food," I said, "I bet this compost will grow incredible strawberries."

"Forget it, Riley. That's as close to a criminal record as I want to get. Gneville can put his worms into a drug rehabilitation program. *We're* taking a course on plant identification."

RILEY ROCKS

Come one, come all!
This rock shall fly
From its firm base
as soon as I

— Sir Walter Scott

Something's wrong, I thought to myself. It was early summer, a Sunday morning. The sun was shining, the birds were singing, the fragrance of honeysuckle draped over the front porch was competing with the aroma of my fresh coffee. With Cynthia at church, and Mace and Juice doing time, the neighbourhood was peaceful.

I should have been relaxed, but something was bothering me. I was sitting on the front steps, flipping pebbles at Cynthia's gnome as I contemplated the 'curb appeal' of my yard. I couldn't figure out what it needed. I don't like to manipulate the landscape too much, but in an effort to make the front yard maintenance free I'd redesigned it the previous year. Still, something wasn't quite right.

The front yard is relatively formal—for me that is. It has patches of gravel and patches of plants: sedum and lavender, phlox and geranium. Kind of a xeriscape. I'd even ripped out the small lawn, partly in the hope it would be less of an attraction to the incontinent Stay, a deranged Irish Setter with a grudge against my grass. Stay's owners called him Stay because they'd spent weeks trying to train him to, but he wouldn't sit still; he always came. Consequently, the name stuck. Removing the grass hadn't helped; he still visited daily.

I was jolted out of my musing by the noisy return of Cynthia as she roared into the driveway, muffler rumbling, radio blaring. She burst from the car with her irritating enthusiasm, slamming the door behind her. Cynthia in a bad mood is loud; in a good mood she's louder. We are perfect opposites in so many ways, but we did seem to be getting along reasonably well, and tried not to aggravate each other. At least *I* tried.

"What's up, Riley?" she hollered across the driveway. "Lost a nickel?"

"Very funny. No I haven't, but something *is* missing here and I can't figure out what it is."

"Well, it's obvious isn't it."

"It is?"

"Yes, it is. If you had more flare for design instead of letting your plants have autonomy you'd see it too. Your yard is in a state of botanical anarchy. What you need is a rock to anchor things. A really big rock, there, right there in the middle of that useless pile of gravel."

"That useless pile of gravel happens to provide contour, and it has strategic importance in the deterrence of Stay, and the occasional cat."

"So that's why it's piling up in my yard. Judging by the evidence of Stay's visits you've got a lousy aim. A rock would be much better."

"A rock? I'm only trying to scare it away, Cynthia, not kill the dumb thing."

"You know what I mean. A rock would be more distinct. It would slow the walker down, cause a detour and allow them to meander, to admire the flowerbeds. Although with your sense of colour I don't see much to admire, your flowerbeds look like tie-dyed old shirts. You need a rock as a distraction."

Despite her comments Cynthia had something. She'd dedicated herself to studying garden design and, besides improving on Edgar's ideas, she was making a name for herself as a garden writer. I took her suggestion seriously.

"You know, you're right. It does need a rock. I was about to reach the same conclusion, and I know where to find the perfect one for this meticulously created landscape."

"Meticulous? Give me a break, Riley. Your idea of meticulous is a lawn mowed with a weed whacker."

"It works."

"Sure it works, about as well as that stinky dog

repellent you tried. I'm surprised you get any mail delivered."

"Never mind that. I've been driving past this beautiful rock everyday on my way to work. It's limestone, all riddled with holes like Swiss cheese. It'll be perfect, except it's so darn big you'll have to help me with it."

"Why me?"

"It was your idea. And as someone with a flare for design, you'd surely want to see your vision realised."

"Okay, Riley. Since you put it so nicely, I'll help."

"Great, we'll fetch it tomorrow."

The following afternoon we set out together. I'd loaded the truck with rock-retrieval equipment: Picks, shovels, crow bar, planks, and a hand winch. Everything we might need to coax a rock out of the field and into the back of the truck. We stopped to load up with coffee and donuts, then drove to the outskirts of town where my rock waited, perched on the wrong side of a water filled ditch.

"There it is," I said eagerly, as we approached. "Oblivious to its fate at the hands of rapacious land developers. It must have been dragged here by some farmer after breaking one too many ploughshares."

"Forget the prose, Riley. How are you going to get it across the ditch?"

"Easy. After you've dug the sod off, we'll just roll it across the planks."

"Sod off? You can sod off. It's your rock. You dig it

out. I'll help roll it."

I dug the grass from around the rock, only to discover more rock.

"You'll have to dig deeper, Riley."

"Thanks for the encouragement, Cynthia." I kept digging. I was determined to have that rock.

"I tell you what," I groaned, as I heaved on the pick. "The farmer who dragged it here must have had a darn impressive team of Clydesdales."

"If that's so. It'll take more than one silly ass to move it now."

"Ha, ha. Hand me the crowbar."

"Why?"

"To move the rock, don't worry."

With the rock undermined we were able to lever it onto the planks where it could be safely rolled across the ditch. But at the halfway point it made a leap for freedom.

"Look out," Cynthia screamed, a trifle slowly I thought afterwards. I sprang away like a startled frog as the rock cannonballed into the ditch. "Well done, Riley. What are you going to do now, teach it to swim? It looks like a baby hippo sitting there half submerged."

"What to do now? Use the winch of course," I said, undaunted. "I'm always prepared. I earned a scout badge in winching. Here, hook it to the bumper while I fasten the cable round the rock. This should be easy. Okay, now stand clear. I'll take up the slack first."

"Go ahead, I'm going to grab a donut."

I took hold of the handle and began to crank furiously. The cable slowly grew taut. It was a hot day and the sweat was soon running into my eyes, making it hard to see, but I could feel something moving. Except it wasn't the rock. I heard a muffled scream and turned just in time to see Cynthia leap from the cab spluttering donut and slopping coffee down her sweater. I scrambled out of the way as the truck teetered on the edge of the ditch before sliding in to join the rock.

"Oh no." I groaned, seriously daunted.

"Oh no? Is that all you can say you idiot. You almost killed me."

"Calm down. It isn't the Grand Canyon you know."

"Not the ditch you fool. I nearly choked on a donut."

"I didn't mean the ditch, I meant your mouth. It isn't the Grand Canyon, at least not quite."

"You'll pay for that one, Riley."

"You deserved it. You shouldn't stuff so much in. What were you doing in the truck anyway? You should have been keeping an eye on things."

"If you must know I was hungry. Oh here, boy scout, have a donut. What are you going to do now? Do you belong to an automobile association? No, of course not. It's time you realised doing it yourself has its limits."

Cynthia's tirade was interrupted by a squeal of

brakes. An old blue truck lurched to a halt. On the door, hand painted, it said, *D'Wayne's Toeing*.

"We might be in luck, Cynthia, if this *is* a tow truck, and not a roving chiropodist."

The driver wound down the window. "Need help, folks?" he growled, biting the end off a cigar big enough to seriously undermine the Helms-Burton Bill. "D'Wayne's towing at your service."

"How did you get here so fast?" I asked.

"Spotted you from the top of the hill," D'Wayne said, through a cloud of smoke and exhaust. "It's not too busy this time of day, so I sit up there with my binoculars. It's amazing what you can see with the late afternoon sun shining into those win... er... I've been watching you for the last hour. I haven't seen anything so funny since a turkey trailer flipped on the highway ramp, just before Thanksgiving."

"Never mind turkeys, D'Wayne," Cynthia said. "Can you pull the truck out of the ditch?"

"Sure, how much money do you have?"

I searched my pockets and emptied my wallet. "Thirty-five dollars."

"Not enough," D'Wayne sneered, putting the truck into gear.

"Wait a minute! Cynthia, how much cash do you have?"

"Me? It's not my truck."

"Come on, you know I'll pay you back."

"I do?"

"Would I dare not?"

"I guess not. Weed my yard and it's a deal."

"Weed your yard?"

"It's your truck, Riley."

"You really enjoy kicking a guy when he's down don't you?"

"Never a better time, never a better time. I told you you'd pay for that crack about the Grand Canyon. Here, I have forty-seven dollars.

"Is that enough?" I asked D'Wayne.

"Eighty-two dollars—close. Any donuts left in that box ma'am?"

"Three," Cynthia frowned.

"Okay, give me the money and hand over the donuts."

D'Wayne stuffed the cash into a swollen billfold, removed the cigar from his mouth and wolfed down the donuts. He then got out of the truck, stuck the cigar back in his mouth and began hooking a cable to the front bumper.

"Have her out in a jiffy," he said, switching on the winch. I shuddered as a horrible wrenching sound came from under my truck, then stared in dismay as the front bumper abandoned it.

"Must have a bit of corrosion there," D'Wayne said. "That's a good thing to know. I'll try hooking onto the frame next."

"Are you sure?" Cynthia said. "Pulling it out a piece at a time doesn't seem too efficient, D'Wayne."

I closed my eyes and covered my ears. I had a vision of two trucks and a rock sitting in the ditch, but this time it held and D'Wayne dragged my truck slowly out of the ditch.

"Looks easy doesn't it, Riley?" Cynthia said. "I bet he has a *real* badge in winching. Why don't you ask him to lift the rock out too while he's at it?"

"Sure, if I get a second mortgage he might deliver it to my house as well."

"Well, if *you* won't ask him, *I* will."

She went over to speak to D'Wayne, and returned smiling. "He says he'll do it, but only if you deliver a case of beer to his place before sundown."

"Is that all?"

"Well I did mention I might have some more donuts at home."

"Great, Cynthia. That'll save a lot of work, and he'll be able to drop the rock in exactly the right place."

"Okay. I'll ride with D'Wayne while you go for the beer. Don't worry, I'll show him precisely where to put the rock."

On my way to the beer store, I stopped at a bank machine for more cash, then followed the directions to D'Wayne's. I left the beer at the gate. There was no way I was venturing into his junkyard alone. It only took an excremental calculation to see his guard dog was a monster compared to Stay.

It was almost dark by the time I turned onto my street. A wonderful feeling of satisfaction came over me as the headlights picked out a familiar grey object. My rock, my beautiful rock.

"What the?" I stomped on the brakes and leapt from the truck. The feeling of satisfaction turned to rage as I raced up to Cynthia's door. I pounded on it.

"You get out here right now and explain this."

"Quiet, Riley," Cynthia said as she opened the door, "you'll disturb the neighbours."

"They're already disturbed—especially you. Why is my rock in your front yard?"

"I don't know. I guess D'Wayne made a mistake. I gave him precise instructions about where to place it before he dropped me at the corner to pick up donuts. You know, it really looks at home there. It would be a shame to move it. I will return your gravel if you like."

I was fuming as I stormed away, speechless at the injustice. And she even had the nerve to call out, "Don't forget, you promised to weed my yard."

I didn't speak to Cynthia for over a week. I would have born the grudge much longer, but for the strangest thing. Stay quit visiting my yard completely. He was attracted to the rock. I could only guess it harboured some rural odour that appealed to him. I didn't mention this phenomenon to Cynthia. In fact I complimented her on her flare for design.

GNOME GNAPPERS

Annihilating all that's made
To a green thought
in a green shade.

— Andrew Marvell

"They got three more last night."

"No! I don't believe it. Why can't they catch the creeps and lock them up? The neighbourhood isn't safe any more."

It was mid September, one of those crisp sunny days that are perfect for fall cleanup. Except it's Cynthia's yard I'm cleaning up. I'm helping her clear out her vegetable garden.

"You're right, Cynthia, first rocks, now gnomes."

"I did not steal your rock, Riley; in fact I paid for most of it, which is why you're down on your knees weeding. Besides, you can see it any time you like. I just happen to have custody, which is a far cry from ripping off garden statuary. I tell you, if anything needs ripping off around here it's that stupid dog that's always hanging around. He's making an awful mess in my front yard."

I smiled to myself as Cynthia continued. "Anyway, I know if I get my hands on a gnome thief he'll be limping on both legs for a very long time." As she said this she wrenched a dead broccoli plant out by the roots. I winced.

"Come on, Cynthia, you're being sexist. How can you be so sure it's a he?"

"Huh, you don't think a woman could do such a despicable thing do you? It's probably a gang of punks reared on heavy metal music videos. It's too bad no one reads fairy stories to kids any more."

"Good thing too. Can you imagine what you'd get combining the brothers Grimm with Ozzy Osborne at an impressionable age? That'd be enough to warp anyone, including girls. Gosh, Cynthia, I shudder to think what they'd do to a poor gnome."

"Riley, you're sick. In any event, by my reckoning that makes thirteen gnomes and one Buddha, 'cept I think they snatched the Buddha by mistake; the clowns probably don't know the difference."

"They got some clowns too?"

"Pay attention. I said I think the Buddha was a mistake. The poor Hamsons are heartbroken. They were quite attached to him. Mr. Hamson used to say 'Good morning buddy' everyday as he left for work."

"I don't know why the Hamsons had a Buddha on their front lawn anyway. They certainly don't have

Buddhist attitudes, not the way old Hamson pours toxic chemicals on his front lawn. The amount he uses would kill off a good-sized rain forest. Mrs. Hamson must be the only living organism around their place. At least I think she's living, she doesn't move much."

"Oh shut up, Riley. You're rambling again. I want to know what we're going to do about these gnome thieves?"

"I don't care. I don't own a gnome, and yours is safe since we've been putting it in the garage every night. In fact I wish they would steal it. I'm tired of lugging the stupid thing around."

"How dare you call Manfred stupid. As concerned citizens we should be trying to catch those creeps."

"And how would you do that? They aren't likely to come around here again now all the gnomes are gone. Of course they might if you left Manfred out."

"Leave him out? You'd love to see him stolen wouldn't you? I don't know why you hate him so much, he's so sweet."

"I don't hate him, I just wish he could walk around on his own, then he could lock *himself* in the garage."

"If he could walk around on his own we'd have no trouble catching the thieves. He could lead us right to them."

"Oh, you mean you need a walking talking Gnome. Well I know where there is one."

"A live gnome? Don't be ridiculous, Riley. It's bad enough you believing Elvis is pumping gas in Thunder Bay."

"He sure looked like Elvis. Anyway, I don't mean a real gnome, well maybe I do. What about Gneville, he's gnomish. I nearly dragged *him* into the garage the other evening. If we dressed him to look like Manfred, and set him out front as a decoy, someone might try to grab him."

"And what if they did? You'd be an accessory to kidnapping."

"I'm not serious. But just think. He'd only have to yell and run into the house while I got their licence number. You'd call the police and then we'd sit back and watch the action. Course, Gneville would be expensive."

"Don't be silly. Gneville is always willing to help his Aunt Cynthia."

"Sure, especially when Aunt Cynthia is stuffing his favourite jelly donuts into him."

"Are you suggesting Gneville is overweight?"

"Not really, at least not when you compare him to the height and weight charts for the average gnome. And another thing, how would you clothe Gneville? As far as I can tell Manfred, has only one outfit, and it's painted on. Even though kids are sporting multi-coloured hair these days, I doubt Gneville would take too kindly to getting a paint job. You'd have to sew something up specially for him." The seemingly innocent comment had barely left my mouth before I realised my blunder.

Cynthia's eyes narrowed. "That sounds an awful lot like a sexist remark. Why me? Can't men sew? Go ahead. Wheedle your way out of it." I tried.

"Lots of men can sew, especially sailors."

"Are you a sailor?"

"No."

"Can you sew?"

"Well, no, but I hemmed these jeans."

"I noticed. Hot glue gun, right?"

"Of course, why not take advantage of man's technology?"

"Have you washed them and had them in the dryer yet?"

I can recognise a last word when I hear one, so I shut up. I'd lost yet another battle of the sexes, but at least the victory had restored her good mood.

"Tell you what, Riley. You've been such a big help weeding; I'll buy you supper. I think you deserve it. I planned to eat out anyway because I'm going to a garden seminar later this evening."

"Another one?

"Yes, another one. I have to learn all I can if I'm to be a successful garden writer. I still have to earn a living you know."

"I may love gardening, Cynthia, but you're getting

obsessed with it."

"I'm not obsessed. I'm just passionate. I've wasted far too many years competing in the rat world, trying to get ahead. Now I've found my joy, I aim to pursue it. It's so relaxing."

"Gardening's like that, brings you down to earth so to speak. You're certainly a lot more relaxed now than when you first moved in."

"Oh I am. I bet you thought I was a real tyrant."

"Oh no, not at all, just angry."

"You'd be angry too if... Never mind. Let's go eat. I'll be late back so you mustn't forget about putting Manfred in the garage."

"By myself? He's heavy you know."

"Course I know, but you want supper don't you?"

"Since you put it like that, I'll do it. I'm starving."

We had an enjoyable meal out together, and passed the time discussing gardening—what else? We talked about everything, from the benefits of composting, to the aesthetics of garden statuary. Afterwards, Cynthia went on to her seminar while I returned home, worn out after all the weeding I'd been doing.

I wanted to go right to bed, but first I had to move Manfred into the garage. Cynthia may have a flare for design, but she doesn't seem to understand what an eyesore her gnome is. I half wished he would get stolen. I'd even toyed with the idea of putting signs at the end of the street, like for a garage sale—*Gnome at # 39*. I didn't have the heart though; she really loved the dumb thing.

I grabbed hold of Manfred and gave a heave. He weighed a ton. I should have used the wheelbarrow. I'd only taken a couple of steps when I slipped on something and crashed into the flowerbed. "That bloody dog," I swore. I lay there, wrestled to the ground by a garden gnome.

I shoved him off and got up, then went over to the Hamsons, where I spent five minutes cleaning my boots on their grass before returning for round two. That's when I noticed. "Oh Jeez," I groaned. When we'd fallen his left ear had broken off. Cynthia would kill me.

I stood Manfred up and ran to the garage in a panic, grabbed some glue, stuck the ear back on then wrapped it with duct tape to hold it. I couldn't move him 'til the glue had set, so I went in to get cleaned up. I intended to put him in the garage later, but after taking a shower I fell asleep on the couch.

When I woke up it was after eleven. I hurried out to move Manfred before Cynthia got home; she wouldn't be too pleased to see him still out front, especially with duct tape around his head. I had mixed emotions over what I discovered. No gnome. Gone, obviously stolen. I felt terrible, even worse when I pictured Cynthia's reaction. She'd go seismic.

However, just for a moment I also felt joy at the marvellous feeling of gnomelessness. It soon passed. I still had to face Cynthia.

I stayed awake the rest of the night trying to concoct a credible explanation for her. If she thought I'd been responsible in any way for Manfred being stolen, I'd need to be in a witness protection program.

I fretted all night, trying to think of an excuse. It wasn't until the sun came up that I thought of the solution, *broad daylight.* Of course! Cynthia had gone straight to her seminar from the restaurant. Manfred had been stolen in *broad daylight,* while *we* were out enjoying ourselves. I was blameless—almost, but I still had to break the bad news.

As I knocked on Cynthia's door I tried to maintain the calm sincerity of an overworked undertaker. When she opened the door though I blurted it out, "They stole Manfred in broad daylight yesterday evening while we were gone." Then I cringed.

Her response wasn't what I expected.

"I know," she said. "I heard it on the news as I drove home."

"You did?"

"Yes, well I guessed. They announced that four more garden gnomes had been snatched in a daring daylight raid, so I checked the garage when I got home. I realised what must have happened when I saw Manfred wasn't in there. Poor Riley, you must have been frantic."

"Er, yes, I was, but I'm feeling better now. Is there anything I can do for you? Can I make you breakfast or something? You look as though you need it."

"Oh thank you, Riley, you're being very kind. I'm starting to rely on you so much."

Wow, I thought. There may be a lot of good come out of this gnome business, besides improvements to the streetscape.

For the next few days Cynthia moped around the house. I didn't see much of her, except when I took her an herbal tea from time to time. Although I wasn't the thief, I felt guilty about Manfred's disappearance. The feeling went away though when I looked at the empty space out front, and it would stay away as long as she didn't replace him. When she told me she couldn't possibly own another gnome I was overjoyed.

As the weeks passed things returned to normal. There'd been no more reports of gnomes being stolen and it looked as if Cynthia had put it all behind her. Then one fall morning we were out planting tulips together when the phone rang. Cynthia answered it.

"You have? They did? Where? Right now? Whoopee, I'm on my way." She turned to me beaming, "Come on, Riley, let's go."

"Go where?"

"Down to the police station. They've recovered the

gnomes, all seventeen of them, and the Buddha."

"Did they catch whoever stole them?"

"Yes, and you won't believe it. It was a group of old folks from the 'Happy Days' budget retirement home. There goes my fairy story theory."

"*Once a punk, always a punk,* I say."

"Yes, I guess even punks grow old, Riley."

"'Happy Days' was asking for trouble; they don't have cable. How were they discovered?"

"The one with the Buddha confessed."

"I'm not surprised. Eight weeks with Buddha in the bedroom, and anyone would see the light."

"Maybe you should get one, Riley. Anyhow, we have to go now and identify Manfred."

"Great. So that means you'll be getting him back."

"Yes, isn't it wonderful. I've missed him so much."

"Me too, Cynthia, me too." Like I miss aphids.

By the time we reached the police station quite a crowd had gathered. It seemed everyone claiming a gnome had brought their families along for the occasion. I'd never seen so many happy people. They were all standing around laughing and joking, sharing gnome stories.

"There's nothing like disaster relief to bring people together, Cynthia."

"Don't be so cynical, Riley."

"Well, listen to them."

"We picked ours up at a garage sale—they had no

idea of his value."

"Do you remember when we repainted him and the colours ran?"

"Ours is a rare Bavarian."

"You must come over and see his sister."

"Sickening."

Cynthia ignored me and went to join the gnomenuts. I stood alone in a corner watching as a couple of police officers lined up all the gnomes for the identity parade. Talk about *Lord of the Rings*. Tolkien should have been there. They were in all shapes and sizes: plastic and concrete, some moss-covered, others garishly painted, some were fishing, some digging, some just standing around, a very familiar one with duct tape wrapped around its head, and the Buddha, looking a little uncomfortable.

While we waited I began idly counting to myself. Fifteen, sixteen, seven... "O-oh! Cynthia—*Cynthia!*"

"What do you want, Riley? Can't you see I'm busy? This is so exciting."

"It's going get a lot more exciting in a few minutes."

"What do you mean?"

"Count the gnomes. I only see sixteen. There were seventeen stolen." She counted.

"You're right. There's one missing."

"Too bad it isn't Manfred," I muttered.

"What did you say?"

"I said I'm glad it isn't Manfred."

"Yes. Thank goodness he's here, although I don't know why he's got duct tape wrapped around his head. I hope he hasn't been abused."

"Abused? There's a lot of weirdos out there, but surely not a gnomophiliac."

"*Riley!*"

One by one the gnomes were reunited with their owners, until only Manfred and Buddha were left.

"Just as I thought," Cynthia said, "The Hamsons aren't here. I knew they didn't really care for him."

"Huh, I realised that when they replaced Bud with a turtle. Go ahead. Sign for Manfred and let's get the heck out of here."

Cynthia stepped forward, but as she did so an old guy made a grab for the gnome. Before you knew it both he and Cynthia had their arms locked around Manfred, hurling abuse at each other. Talk about bizarre. It took five cops to separate them. They kept arguing until the sergeant threatened to throw them both in a cell if they didn't calm down.

"Now," he said, "We have a little problem here. One gnome, two gnome claimants, and a Buddha. We can settle this in a civilised manner. Since the gentleman arrived first I suggest you take the Buddha and let him have his gnome."

"What do you mean," Cynthia said. "It isn't his gnome. It's my gnome. And I don't want the Buddha."

She then went on to suggest he and the old man were related—to a gnome. This probably biased his decision.

"If you're so sure it's your gnome you should be able to identify it. You should have scratched your name on the bottom or something, but you didn't, so take the Buddha and get out of here."

Two cops held Cynthia as the old guy picked up Manfred. She turned to me, tears in her eyes, "Please, Riley, you have to do something. Don't let them take him away."

I was torn. Here was my chance to be rid of Manfred forever, except the look on Cynthia's face stirred something in me.

"Hold it," I said, stepping forward. "I can identify the gnome."

"You can," glared the sergeant. "How?"

I felt like Sherlock Holmes. "I think, Sergeant, that if you carefully remove that piece of duct tape, you'll find the ear has been recently glued on."

On the way home Cynthia couldn't stop thanking me. I basked in the glory, thinking that putting up with Manfred might have its consolations, until she turned to me and said, "Tell me, Riley, how did you know the ear had been glued on?" My knuckles whitened on the steering wheel.

"Lucky guess, Cynthia, lucky guess."

WET BODY PARTS

To dig and delve in nice clean dirt
can do a mortal little hurt.

— John Kendrick Bangs

"What do you think of ponds, Riley?" Cynthia asked, as she slid a large slice of rhubarb pie in front of me. "It seems they're the thing to have these days."

"So are pitbulls, do you want one of those? I hear they're great for getting rid of large garden pests."

"Then you'd better behave, buddy, or I may get one."

"I'll do anything you like if it means more pie."

"Thanks, Riley. I'll keep that in mind."

Cynthia had kindly invited me in for coffee and commiseration over the non arrival of spring. As she made the coffee I sat at the kitchen table flipping through a magazine which featured an article on water gardening. She'd taken more garden courses over the winter, and I saw this as further evidence of her determination to have the perfect yard.

"Seriously though," she continued, "don't you think

a pond would blend in well with Edgar's landscaping?"

"I suppose it might, anything to knock some of the sharp edges off."

"You can't stand things neat and tidy, can you?"

"I can't stand unnatural precision. It grates on me. I'm more of a Walden Pond kind of guy."

"Oh, you mean you do like ponds?"

"No, I meant Walden Pond the book. You know—Henry David Thoreau. He was the original minimalist, preferred the simple life, not interested in what the rest of the world was doing. You should be more like him, Cynthia, uninfluenced by trends, satisfied with the way things are."

"Just shows how much you know me. I do like simplicity, and ponds are simple."

"Simple? They're about as simple as multi-lingual assembly instructions. And they're a lot of work."

"What do you mean they're a lot of work? You're too negative. A well maintained pond takes care of itself. I've been reading up on them."

"I don't mean they're a lot of work to maintain. It's the digging, the waterfall building, you know, all those rocks."

"What's the matter? Is your back starting to ache? You're acting as though you've got a warning light flickering on. You're still a young man, relatively speaking."

"Thanks a lot." I did have a warning light on—

my work alert—and it was flashing brightly.

"Have another piece of pie, Riley. It is your favourite isn't it? Anyway, I've decided. I want a pond and I need your help."

I groaned. It's not that I mind helping Cynthia. We just never seem able to agree on the way to go about things. I suppose it's because I am more of the Walden Pond type. I do prefer the simple life. After years of planning and pruning, not to mention a lot of backbreaking work, my yard is the way I like it.
If I need to look at a pond I can get in the car and drive out to the country. Unfortunately, I hadn't counted on her enthusiasm for water. Perhaps because it had been a long winter, or maybe because TV was into reruns, or, I thought afterwards, it might have been the fresh rhubarb pie, but for whatever reason I found myself offering to help.

"Thanks, Riley. Let's get started."

"What, right now?"

"Of course," she said, shoving the rhubarb pie back into the fridge. "There's no time to waste. I want to have it finished by the end of May, in time to be selected for the charity garden tour. A pond should clinch it."

It probably would. Edgar had almost made it onto the garden tour a couple of times. If he hadn't cursed the chair of the selection committee for stepping on the grass he would have. Ever since I'd mentioned this to

Cynthia, it had become a goal to have her garden featured on the tour. Now she was unstoppable.

"Wait a minute, Cynthia," I said. "Slow down. You have to have plans. You can't rush into ponds; you have to approach them carefully. Have you been reading up on them? Or have you just been looking at glossy magazines? They don't reveal the whole picture you know. I've seen more reality on the World of Disney."

"You have a point, Riley, but I'm so excited. I can just picture beautiful water lilies with exotic fish swimming among them."

"And mosquitoes, don't forget the mosquitoes."

"The fish will eat the mosquitoes."

"They will? Are you getting flying fish?"

"Don't be stupid. You know what I mean. The fish will eat the mosquito larvae."

"Then you'd better get some piranha. And another thing, have you thought about where you'd like to locate it?"

"I see it beside the Patio. The sound of water trickling over rocks is supposed to be relaxing. My therapist says I need to relax more."

"Therapist! I hope you didn't pay her. I could have told you that for nothing."

"When I want your advice I'll ask for it. Now what's wrong with it near the patio?"

"All that splashing water will put a damper on any

conversation, your guests will be continually going to the washroom, and you'll be well within range of the mosquitoes when they're hungry. You'd be better off with it down the yard a ways, slightly out of sight. Then someone exploring your yard can discover it serendipitously and be astonished at its beauty. Course, you don't want it to be too hidden. I can just imagine your guests disappearing around the forsythia—splish, splash, scream. You know there is a low spot back near the cedar. It would sure save a lot of digging if you placed it there."

"Perfect. I never thought of that. What a great idea, Riley."

"In that case can I have more pie?"

"You can have more pie when the pond is dug. We'll start tomorrow. If you can believe the weather forecast, it's supposed to be sunny and dry, a perfect spring day."

Cynthia's eyes were shining with excitement and her hair looked more frightening than ever. She was on a mission. Even I had to admit some grudging enthusiasm. It would be nice to get out in the yard and work on a project again, even if it was Cynthia's.

The following morning Spring arrived suddenly, as it always does in these parts, causing crocus to materialise like they'd beamed down from another planet. For once the weather forecast was accurate.

"Good morning, Riley. What a beautiful day.

Spring has arrived at last."

"Sure has. Better late than never, but still twelve weeks after that stupid groundhog predicted it would arrive. Any gardener knows there's always three more months of winter after Groundhog Day. Spring comes when I see a groundhog on the highway, wheel-bait. A shadow of its former self. Come on, let's get started. We'll need some string to define the shape of it, or better yet, maybe the garden hose."

Cynthia fetched the hose, and then we spent half an hour arguing about the best shape. She was fixated on a kidney design. I disagreed. "Kidney? Come on Cynthia, surely we can be more creative. Everyone has kidneys: kidney shaped ponds, kidney shaped swimming pools, kidney shaped dishes. Why not something unique in pond design? Be bold! How about a trapezoid, or an eggplant? Even a spleen. Anything but a kidney. And anyway, shouldn't kidneys always be in pairs?"

"It's my yard, my pond, and it's going to be my kidney."

I gave up, "Left or right?"

We marked the outline of the pond, stripped off the turf and piled it up for composting. Then we dug out the topsoil. Cynthia had it in mind to use it to enlarge a flowerbed, but it was so thin she barely had enough to fill a planter.

"The creeps!" she fumed. "Only two inches of soil.

No wonder the grass dries out so fast. How dare they."

"Don't be so surprised. These houses were only built twenty years ago. What did you expect? All your topsoil went to finance time-share developments in Florida."

Cynthia leaned on her shovel. "This sounds like another of your conspiracy theories. Go on."

"Well, you see, not all developers are scrupulous. When they prepare land for construction, the first thing they do is strip off the topsoil, sometimes a couple of feet of it. Then they gouge out holes for foundations. This is a problem. What to do with all the leftover subsoil? It's far too expensive to truck it away, so they just spread it out evenly. After they're done they scatter a bit of soil on top and lay the turf."

"So what happens to the topsoil that's left over, there must be mountains of it."

"There are. It's bought by a soil cartel."

"You're joking."

"It's true! They mix it with manure. Manure's piling up faster than the National Debt. Instead of ploughing it back into the land, too many farmers are still slopping synthetic fertilisers on everything instead. They're all desperate to get rid of it."

"Same as the debt."

"Right! Next they throw in some peatmoss, package it in brightly coloured plastic bags, complete with convenient carry handle. And there you have it, readily available at your local grocery store. An overpriced bag of dirt produced for nothing by Mother Nature; processed, packaged, and sold back to you so you can return it to its original location. The profits must rival those of the drug trade."

"Sounds like a great plot for the X-Files. You may have it all figured out, Riley, but what exactly are we going to do with this subsoil?"

"Well the logical thing to do would be rebury it."

"Bury it? Where do we bury it?"

"I don't know, it's up to you. It is your yard. If you don't feel like burying it you could pile it up in a corner and mix a little with your garbage each week; however, that's risky. Garbage guys get really upset when they discover a pail-padder. A friend of mine tried it and he woke up to find his front yard looking like a landfill site. They must have dumped the whole truck. No, if I were you I'd bury it. Your veggie patch could use a little raising up. We'll just dig a big hole for it. The topsoil there is deep because old Edgar trucked... er, well anyway."

"You know, I'm beginning to sympathise with the land developers."

Three days later we'd managed to dig out the subsoil, and the subclay, and even a small mountain of stones, all of which we reburied at the bottom of the veggie garden. Then it rained. An April deluge. Three more days passed before we ventured out into the yard again. I joined Cynthia as she gazed despondently at her premature pond.

"Looks like you have your pond sooner than you expected, Cynthia. Too bad it has to be emptied to put the liner in."

"I could strangle somebody."

"I warned you ponds were a lot of work."

"You don't need to tell me, Riley. My back hurts just as much as yours."

"Come on then. Let's get started."

We spent the whole morning bailing mud and water. Then it rained again, which meant more mud because the edges kept sliding into the hole. By the time we got it cleaned out the yard had taken on the colour and texture of Vimy Ridge, circa 1916, with a very realistic shell crater.

Luckily it stayed dry for a few days and we were finally able to get the liner in and refill the pond with clean water. But the work wasn't over. Cynthia baked another rhubarb pie, then insisted I accompany her on a tour of the countryside to collect rocks for the pond edging. I agreed, on condition we limit the size, which meant we needed a lot, so we spent a whole Saturday cruising country roads picking up rocks. It was worth it though. I didn't want another encounter with D'Wayne.

"You know what, Cynthia," I said, tossing another rock into the truck. "Bertrand Russell, the great philosopher, believed most human activity appeared to be devoted to moving material around close to the surface of the earth. He must have built a pond."

"Only once I bet," she grunted, as she heaved a small boulder onto the tailgate. "Thank goodness we're almost finished. And thank you, Riley. I couldn't have done it without you."

"Thank goodness is right. When I've recuperated enough I plan to get my veggie garden turned over. By which time it will probably be too late to plant anything this year."

"Don't be such a grouch. I'll help you. I just have to do some planting and the pond will be complete. Next Sunday we'll have the official dedication or whatever. Gneville is coming over. He wants to release his pet gold fish, Hot Lips."

"Hot Lips? What kind of a name is that? It sounds like a stage name for a stripper."

"He called it that because the lips were all red—How do you know what strippers call themselves, Riley?"

"I don't...I mean I just guessed. I hope you don't think I... I read a lot."

"Sure, Riley. Anyway, he says it needs a bigger place to live."

"Huh! More likely he's tired of feeding it."

By the following weekend the plants were planted, including Cynthia's precious water lilies, the fish were launched, and the yard cleaned up. At last we were able to stand back and admire our work, and I mean work.

"I have to admit, Cynthia, it does look lovely, but I'm not sure about the shape. When the edges slid in it changed a bit." I walked around the pool to gain a different perspective. "I'm not sure what it looks like now, definitely not a kidney. Maybe a.... Wait a minute. I don't believe it. When you stand over here beside the cedar it looks exactly like a..." I tried not to laugh. "Here, stand right here."

"What are you talking about?"

"I'm talking about body parts. You've really got yourself a unique design. You won't see this in a magazine. Hot Lips will be right at home here. Look! Stand right on this exact spot."

"Oh no, oh, Riley, you're right." She began to giggle. Then we both burst into laughter. We were laughing so hard we didn't hear Gneville arrive. He rounded the forsythia suddenly, startling us. Cynthia lost her balance, teetered for a moment on the edge, then tumbled backwards into the pond—but not before grabbing my sleeve. Meanwhile Gneville collapsed in joy at the serendipitous discovery of two adults floundering in a fishpond. We clambered out spitting and spluttering, pulling strands of pondweed from our faces.

"Y'know what, Cynthia. I think maybe you'd better plant a big shrub where we were standing, before the selection committee comes around. And perhaps trim the Forsythia back a bit, otherwise you'll never get on the garden tour."

"This time I think I'll take your advice, Riley."

Two weeks later the committee did its inspection, and I knew her dream had come true when she leaned over the fence afterwards and said, "Riley. What kind of pie can I bake you?"

UNWELCOME GUESTS

Thrice blessed are our friends:
they come, they stay,
And presently they go away.
— Richard R. Kirk

"Riley—Riley! What's that disgusting stench coming from your backyard? *Riley!*" The call was more insistent the third time, annoyingly so. It was Cynthia. I looked up from what I was doing, discouraging slugs from making a banquet of my begonias. *Flip, squish, flip, squish.* Such satisfying work. With an old pair of barbecue tongs I clamp them by the foot, or is it the ankle? then I flip them onto the pathway were I show them *my* foot. *Flip, squish, flip, squish.*

"Disgusting stench?" I replied, "I've no idea, unless you mean the satisfying fragrance of slug carcasses rotting in the sun. It will soon pass. I've had a very successful morning."

"Ugh, I'm not sure who's more revolting—you or the slugs, but since you seem to be enjoying it so much you can come over and start on mine. I suppose I can put up with the smell if it means less slugs. I tell you, the more I kill the more there are. They're eating my hostas and I've got the Garden Tour coming in ten days."

This wasn't the moment to admit I'd flipped a few over the fence into her yard—accidentally.

"They are a problem this year, but this is the best solution. I've tried most things."

"Can't you drown them or something?"

"What, drop them in a pail of water? Maybe you could, Cynthia. I'm not that sadistic. *Flip, squish.* They can't swim you know. Can you imagine their final panic-stricken moments as the spark of life is slowly extinguished? Mind you they're so darn sloppy I can't imagine they have much of a spark. If you prefer I'll just pop them in a grocery bag, then you can take them out into the country and set them free. But you realize *you'll* be responsible for people starving, because then they'll ravage great swaths of farmland like some Biblical Plague. You just don't seem to realize what we're up against. Humanity slimed out of existence. That's what happened to the dinosaurs you know—you haven't rolled your eyes yet, Cynthia."

"Carry on Riley. I'm believing every word of it."

"Good, just don't tell anyone. But seriously, I bet palaeontologists never even considered slugs. Course why would anyone stop to consider a slug, unless it's ravaging your rhubarb."

"Okay, okay, stop babbling. There has to be a better way to get rid of the horrible things. What about beer traps? Don't they work?"

"I haven't tried them. I don't think I could face the moral dilemma of having another beer or saving a Begonia, especially as the intended victim would have the pleasure of passing away in a drunken stupor. Trouble is, slugs are incorrigible binge drinkers. They'll travel blocks for a free beer; consequently all the neighbour's slugs show up in the party yard. Then there's the problem of beer attracting other unwelcome guests like Mace and Juice. I don't think you want to see those guys hanging around your place again."

"Now I'm rolling my eyes. I'd sooner put up with slugs. How about slug pellets? Surely they must work."

"Oh the pellets are great at dispatching the odious little omnipeds, but bad for the environment. I tried them once, before I attained environmental consciousness. They're even more enticing than beer. My yard became a cemetery for slugs. Hordes of them were gathering here to die. Bit like those elephant graveyards I suppose. And then I had to deal with all the relatives that came to pay their last respects. Definitely not a good idea. You could end up with your yard being declared a sacred burial ground. Next thing you know, some obnoxious little creep from the city with an overwhelming sense of self-importance, is telling you that you aren't allowed to dig your flowerbeds over."

"Didn't you once work for the city, Riley?"

"Er, yes, well—the pellets are risky. They also attract more than slugs. When I tried them I had to dispose of a whole menagerie of dead critters—two mice, three birds, a black squirrel, and one white rabbit. Sadly no cats."

"Did you say, white rabbit? Gneville lost his pet rabbit, a white one. He was heartbroken."

"Er, kind of. When I said white I meant just the tail. This rabbit was brown and white, mostly brown. Probably wild. In fact, now I think about it—definitely wild, so it couldn't have been Gneville's."

"I hope not, otherwise it will be more than slugs getting squished around here. Gneville loved that rabbit. He called it tripod. The poor thing had only three legs."

I breathed a sigh of relief, secure in the knowledge the slug pellet victim, other than being dead, was not physically challenged.

"You have a point about the pellets, Riley. They're obviously dangerous, and certainly not good for the environment. If we could come up with something that worked, and was safe, we'd make a fortune."

"Toads work, but they're remarkably unfaithful, always hopping off to clean up someone else's yard."

"Who cares if they hop off? If we had enough they'd

be hopping everywhere. They'd still be eating slugs, and they'd clean up the whole neighbourhood. I've seen hundreds out at the conservation area."

"We could go into business, Cynthia, maybe advertise in ***Yard Perfect****—The perfect solution for slug control—TOADS. Environmentally friendly! Efficient! Cheap!* We just catch 'em, ship 'em out by mail-order and the money comes rolling in."

"But would they arrive alive?"

"If not they'd be about as welcome as a letter bomb."

"Listen, maybe we could get a small business loan, banks are always looking for innovative ideas."

"Don't be ridiculous, Cynthia. I was only kidding. What on earth would you ship a toad in anyway? A toad tin, or maybe a toad trunk for bulk orders. I can see it now—*Toads by the Truckload!* Sorry, Cynthia, buy a lottery ticket and keep dreaming. I think you're out to lunch on this one. Speaking of which, *flip, squish,* I am hungry. Let's eat, then take a drive out to the conservation area. I am willing to collect enough toads to help salvage what's left of the begonias. I'm beginning to think slugs have the ability to reincarnate. If they only realized that if they led exemplary lives they might come back as a slightly higher life form. Something like Mace or Juice. Look, I swear I've squished this one at least twice; it has a mole on its left cheek." *Flip, squish.*

"Ugh! Come on then, we'll go for lunch, but let's pick

up Gneville first, I'm sure he'd love to help."

"I'm sure he'd love to eat burgers, you mean."

"Be nice. You know Gneville can be very helpful."

"I suppose so. At least it will get him away from the TV for an hour or too."

"He's only been watching TV a lot because he's upset about his rabbit, this will cheer him up. But please, no more slug talk. And oh, Riley."

"Yes?"

"Change your boots."

We collected the grieving Gneville, who perked up immediately at the mention of lunch. He insisted the best burgers were to be found at the Cholesterol Cafe. As a cholesteroly conscious adult I try to regulate my intake of fat and should eat only veggie burgers, but it's hard to resist peer pressure, especially when your peers number in the billions.

We drove to the closest outlet, where as always the speed and efficiency with which we were served amazed me.

"You know why they're so fast don't you?" I whispered to Cynthia.

"Why?"

"They don't want to give your brain a chance to figure out what exactly the stomach is craving."

"If it bothers you so much you could have a salad you know."

"I considered it, but since this morning I've realized

slugs eat salad, and look what it does for them. Besides, my stomach has gained full control, so a Big Angus Burger it is."

We were handed our order with curt instructions to have a nice day, then found a booth to squeeze into. I'm not large, but it was a tight fit. I complained to Cynthia, who agreed.

"If they are so smart and efficient," she said, "you'd think they'd have figured out the shape of their average customer and sized the booths accordingly."

"They have," mumbled Gneville through a faceful of fries. "They don't want you to get too comfortable, 'cos you'd stay too long. They're always asking me and my friends to leave."

"Right, Gneville, and another thing..."

"Change the subject, Riley. You don't have to eat here you know. I'm trying to enjoy my meal, while you're trying to make me feel guilty about eating it."

"We could talk about toads."

"*Riley.*"

"Okay, okay. So, Gneville, tell me about Tripod. How did your poor rabbit lose a leg?"

"Dog," said Gneville, with a splatter of strawberry milkshake.

"Dog? You mean some nasty great Pitbull attacked him!"

"No, he attacked it. 'Cept it wasn't a pitbull. It was Mr. Sabo's toy poodle. For some reason Tripod kept jumping on it—I don't know why. Course, he wasn't called Tripod then."

"So what happened?"

"Well one day he tore after the poodle and it ran into the house. Mr. Sabo slammed the screen door real quick and my rabbit became Tripod."

"Poor Gneville," Cynthia consoled, "it must have been so upsetting."

"Not really," Gneville smirked, "A rabbit's foot is lucky. They make a great Christmas gift you know." Cynthia went red in the face as the truth dawned on her. I almost choked on a fry as she glared at Gneville.

"Gneville," I said. "How could you?"

"I didn't," he grinned. "Honest, Aunt Cyn, yours is a real one. I mean it wasn't Tripod's. It came from Taiwan. I bought it at the market."

"Enough," said Cynthia. "You're both disgusting. I can't eat another thing. Let's get out of here."

We left the restaurant and drove out to the conservation area where we found a place to park close to the marsh. Cynthia led us single file down a narrow path. It was stinking hot and we hadn't gone very far before all three of us were swatting madly at mosquitoes.

"I may be mistaken," Cynthia said, "but I thought toads were supposed to eat mosquitoes."

"If they do they aren't very hungry," I said, slapping furiously.

"They do," Gneville said, "but only at night. I think toads are nocturnal."

"Gneville," groaned Cynthia, "Why didn't you say so before?"

"Before what?"

"Before we took you for a hamburger," I snarled.

"We could come back this evening," Gneville pleaded, "I don't mind."

"Sure, no doubt after a junkfood supper at the restaurant."

"Okay, okay," Cynthia interrupted, "calm down. Why don't we just go home, rest up, and prepare for the evening? We'll need flashlights and lots of mosquito repellent."

"Wait a minute, Cynthia. If you think I'm coming out here in the dark to chase toads around with a flashlight you're out of your mind."

"Who bought lunch, Riley?"

"You did, Cynthia."

That evening we returned to the conservation area fully equipped to collect toads, only to find the gate locked.

"They close at sunset you know," Gneville remarked.

"They do! Why didn't you tell us?"

"I figured you were planning to climb the fence. Everyone else does."

"But that's against the law," I said, "and I'm not sure collecting toads isn't as well. Is there anything else we should know, Gneville?"

"Probably, but I can't think of it right now."

Against my better judgement we climbed the fence. With Cynthia in the lead we followed the path down to the marsh again. At least this time the mosquitoes were leaving us alone.

"Well, Cynthia, where are all these toads you claim to have seen? I can't say they're exactly hopping wildly to and fro."

"Just ahead, in the clearing by the marsh. Listen! Can't you hear them?"

"I can hear something, I thought it was Gneville grumbling."

"Look! Look right in front of us, hundreds. Quick, you and Gneville start catching them, I'll hold the box open."

"Why me? It wasn't my idea you know."

"But they're your slugs they'll be eating, Riley, so start chasing, and watch where you're stepping."

"Ah jeez."

After half an hour of frantic chasing, Gneville and I had caught about a dozen toads—enough for me to call it a night.

"I think that's plenty, Cynthia."

"How many do we have?"

"Whatever's in the box. We'd better count them. I know you'll be fussy when it comes to dividing the spoils."

I eased up the lid and shone my flashlight in.

"One, two, three. Wait a minute. These aren't toads. They're frogs. We've been collecting frogs."

"What do you mean?" Cynthia said, peeking into the box. "Frogs, toads, they're all the same aren't they?"

"Well they are similar, but I'm sure frogs prefer insects, so they're are no use to us for catching slugs. We have big slugs, which means we need big toads."

"You mean we've been running around the park all night for nothing?"

"Not quite," said Gneville, his outstretched arms straining to hold what looked like a clump of mud the size of a small chicken.

"What a monster," he gasped. "He's a toad isn't he, Riley?"

"He sure is. Dump the frogs, Cynthia. We don't need them. One toad like this is plenty."

"Ugh, he's ugly."

"Careful, you'll hurt his feelings. And anyway you're looking at the wrong end."

"I don't care. I've changed my mind. I think I'd rather look at slugs than look at it. You can keep him in your yard."

"Why thank you, we'll be very happy together. He can't help his looks you know. You are what you eat, just like those folks at the Cholesterol Cafe. I bet he'll eat billions of slugs too."

Cynthia dumped out the frogs and Gneville stuffed

the toad into the box. It barely fit, but looked content. I closed the lid firmly. I'd had enough toad hunting for the evening.

Wearily, we retraced our steps out of the marsh and back to the fence. We were just about to climb over when an amplified voice almost deafened us.

"Freeze." Simultaneously a powerful spotlight blinded us. Like startled rabbits we froze.

"O-oh," Gneville said, "I've remembered the other thing—Ranger Rick. He's a stickler for park regulations."

"Identify yourself and state your reason for being in the conservation area after sundown."

"He sounds like a petty bureaucrat masquerading as Robo Cop." I whispered to Cynthia.

"You said that, Riley, not me."

"Well?" Ranger Rick barked.

"We're looking for a lost rabbit," fibbed Cynthia in a panic. "A tame one. He belongs to my nephew Gneville here."

"A missing rabbit? What colour?"

"White," Gneville answered.

"Like the one over there?" We turned slowly, to find we weren't the only rabbits caught in the headlights.

"Tripod!" whooped Gneville, rushing to retrieve his pet.

"By golly you're lucky to find him son. Okay, stuff it in the box and be on your way."

"I think I'll just carry him if you don't mind."

"Whatever, but next time you lose a pet, report to my office first with a complete description in writing. Let a trained professional do the tracking." Ranger Rick then turned his truck around and sped away, leaving us ducking a shower of gravel.

"Lucky for us Tripod showed up when he did," Cynthia said as we drove home.

"I'll say. I had the feeling Ranger Rick was about to drag us in for interrogation."

"'Cept this isn't Tripod," Gneville said. "It's better. This one has all its feet."

"Then we did all right, Gneville. We get a slug catcher and you get a fully equipped rabbit. Not a bad night's work."

The following day we set the monster toad free in my garden. It immediately hopped under the fence into Cynthia's yard, making itself at home under her deck. In no time Cynthia was banging on my door demanding it be repatriated.

"Get that thing out of my yard, Riley."

"But, Cynthia, I thought you wanted to get rid of your slugs."

"I do, but not if I it means having a cow patty hopping around my yard. How will that look when the garden tour comes through?"

"I can think of worse things, but what will you do about your slugs?"

"*My* slugs? I'm beginning to think the whole problem started in *your* yard anyway."

"Okay, I'll take him. I don't mind having Custer hopping around gorging himself on slugs."

"Custer? Custer the toad? What kind of a name is that?"

"I think it's the perfect name for him—or her. Incidentally, do you know how to tell…? Oh never mind. I don't think political correctness has to extend to toads. I do think it's an appropriate name though. From a begonia's point of view, Custer will be like the Cavalry riding to the rescue. Kind of fits doesn't it?"

"I suppose so, but just keep him out of my yard. I'll just have to come up with some other means of getting rid of the slugs."

"You could try adopting a Buddhist attitude and just accept them as part of some eternal plan, although I'm not sure what part. But since you're just a little too highly strung to be a Buddhist, why don't you hire Gneville to catch them, it's just the kind of job a boy his age would enjoy. You could pay him a dime a dozen."

"I wish you'd thought of that in the first place. We could have saved ourselves a lot of trouble. I'll go call him right now. Hey! What exactly do you mean by highly strung?"

"See you later," I said, retreating to the shed, "I have to go build a toad house for Custer."

The following weekend I was sitting on my patio,

feeling a little disappointed. After some initial success Custer appeared to be on the retreat, or maybe a mono diet didn't suit him. My border was bereft of begonias. It looked as though I'd have to go back to the tedious technique of flipping and squishing. Since it was Sunday, I wasn't feeling too motivated, so I decided to have a beer first and think about it. As I popped the bottle cap there was an unpleasant splat on the deck. Then another, and another. Slugs, flying slugs. I knew they loved beer but leaping a five-foot fence was impossible. They were coming from the direction of Cynthia's yard. I approached the fence cautiously, fearing I'd get slimed—or slugged.

I peered over to discover Gneville, armed with a pair of barbecue tongs.

"*Flip, squish, flip, squish,*" he was saying as he worked away contentedly.

"Hey you little snotnose. What do you think you're doing?"

"Oh, hi, Mister Riley. Would you believe I've already earned enough to buy six burgers?"

"That's nice, but why are you flipping them into my yard? Cynthia won't pay up without proof of pressing."

"Ah, first rule of business is supply and demand. Control supply and you can demand what you like. I have to spare a few for my breeding program."

Like Custer, it was time to retreat.

"Okay, Gneville. How much?"

WILD KINGDOM

This is the garden: colours come and go,
frail azures fluttering from night's outer wing
strong silent greens serenely lingering,
absolute lights like baths of golden snow.

— Edward Estlin Cummings

"Eight hundred people! You're nuts, Cynthia. I didn't think there'd be so many. They'll bring their kids and their dogs. They'll be snipping cuttings and pilfering plants. Who's going to control them? I bet after they've left your place will look like Woodstock—the day after.

"Don't be such a worry wart, Riley. It's extremely well organized, and there'll be volunteers assisting. I don't have anything to worry about. I've been dreaming of this almost since I moved in here. Nothing is going to spoil it, and it is for a very good cause. The garden tour raises a lot of money for charity."

"Come on, Cynthia. You aren't doing it just for charity are you?"

"No, I guess I'm not. I've been competing in a man's world all my life. Gardening just happens to be a level playing field, so I plan to excel on it."

"Playing field is right. That's what it'll look like when it's over. All I can say is: I wouldn't let them through my yard at any price, let alone do it for charity."

"Sometimes I could strangle you, Riley. Don't you care about those less fortunate?"

"Who's less fortunate than me being strangled by you? Oh all right. If it makes you feel any better, I'll help you get things ready.

"That's something I suppose. There is one thing you can do."

"What?"

"Help clean out my compost heap."

"Why? It isn't full. Compost is better the longer it does."

"Does what?"

"Compost of course!"

"I know, but I couldn't help notice a bad smell coming from it the other day."

"Compost doesn't smell, not unless you've been adding something you shouldn't. Have you been putting meat products in your compost?"

"Certainly not!"

"Then it's probably nitrogen build up from too many grass clippings. You have to maintain a balance between carbon and nitrogen to keep a compost pile working you know."

"You really know it all don't you, Riley?"

"I'll ignore that. However, I did take a course once. Do you know what the worst thing is you can put on a compost pile?"

"I'm sure you'll tell me."

"Processed food. It's so full of preservatives it stops the process. Mind you, I'd say you're better off throwing it in the compost pile than eating it. Course, it can save money when a family member who eats junk food exclusively passes away."

"Why's that?"

"There's less embalming required. It's a real problem for the folks who run retirement homes."

"Sure. The problem with you is I never know if you're kidding, or if you really believe this stuff."

"You don't? Good. I wouldn't want to be predictable. Yes, when some old soul kicks off in front of the TV, it can be weeks before anyone realizes. Bodies taking up dead space after their savings have run out can eat into profits."

"Riley, you have the sensitivity of a doorstop. Start digging. I'll feel better when the compost is cleaned out. I have space in the corner of the vegetable garden where we can dig it in."

We got down to work. I don't mind handling compost, it's only pre soil, but there was a strange odour about it.

"You know what, Cynthia? I think something's been living in your compost heap. You have squatters, maybe mice or rabbits."

"Too bad, they're getting evicted. I've no time for vermin in my yard. Present company excepted."

"You're all heart."

We were about halfway done when Gneville arrived, pinching his nose.

"Ugh, what's that horrible smell?"

"I didn't think it was so bad," Cynthia said, "but then my hayfever has been acting up a bit this week, and Riley is always a little stuffy."

"Thanks, Cynthia. Very funny. Where did you find that line, on your face?"

"Keep digging, you."

"So, Gneville, are you here to help your Aunt Cynthia prepare her yard for fame and fortune?"

"What fortune?" Gneville asked, his beady eyes twitching.

"I'm not sure, but with eight hundred potential customers passing through her back yard, there must be some way to take money off them. What do you think, Cynthia? Maybe Gneville could sell souvenirs or something."

"No way, and don't put ideas into his head. This is a very respectable fundraiser; it's not the Olympic Games. I won't have any tacky commercialism on my property."

"I was only joking."

"Keep digging, Riley. You can help too, Gneville. Start moving some compost to the vegetable garden."

Gneville went to fetch a shovel, and as expected it was the last we saw of him. Cynthia and I kept at it and eventually got the pile cleared away; only to find, to my dismay, it had rotted a hole in the fence.

"Cynthia," I grumbled, "what are you going to do about this? Your stinking compost has rotted out my beautiful barn-board fence. You could drive a herd of cattle through this hole. This simply won't do you know."

"Oh, get off your high horse, cowboy. Indignation doesn't become you. I have a few boards in the shed. I'll even nail them up for you."

"Good, the sooner the better. I wouldn't want the garden tourists getting off the beaten path, let alone off your beaten lawn and beaten flower beds."

"You're just jealous. You'll be sorry, especially when I'm featured in 'Landscapers Digest."

"Ha! More like Landfill Disgust."

Cynthia raised her shovel. "How dare you call my yard a landfill?"

I was beginning to realize this garden tour was far more important than my wellbeing. It was a life or death issue for her. Seeing as how I valued my life I shot through the hole in the fence.

"And stay out of my yard, you little creep!" she

yelled after me.

"You couldn't pay me to visit it," I yelled back.

Our neighbourly relationship had been improving steadily, but thanks to the tension generated by the garden tour it was now as shaky as a Mideast peace agreement. I decided to stay clear of her until after the tour, hoping things might get back to normal by then. It was scheduled for the following Sunday, from eleven 'til five.

The rest of the week Cynthia worked frantically in her yard. From dawn to dusk, she weeded, pruned, and snipped. I called over to her once and asked if she wanted to borrow some nail-clippers. She glared at me, then moments later a handful of weeds came flying over the fence.

At ten-thirty on Sunday morning I made myself comfortable on the deck with a cooler of beer and some egg-salad sandwiches. Since my deck overlooks Cynthia's backyard, I had a perfect vantage point to see the show. At ten-fortyfive a car stopped on the street. Two couples got out and began to scrutinize the front yard. They wandered around for a bit, poked and prodded, peered through the front windows, then proceeded to the back, where a beaming Cynthia met them.

"Hello," she said warmly. "Welcome, welcome. You must be the volunteers from the Horticultural Society."

"Er, no," they replied, "we're not volunteering for anything. We just came to see the garden."

"Then you're early," Cynthia said, frowning. "Do you have tickets?"

"No, we don't have tickets."

"You must have tickets. They're ten dollars each, available from the volunteers at any of the eight homes on the tour."

"Can't we pay you?" one of them asked.

"No you can't. My yard may be on the tour, but I have nothing to do with selling tickets. You'll have to wait until the volunteers arrive."

Meanwhile, another car had stopped out front with more garden viewers, then another. Soon a ragged line had formed in the driveway. By eleven-thirty there must have been a hundred people waiting, some not so patiently. Cynthia stood guard at the gate. No one was getting by her without a ticket.

At noon the volunteers finally showed up. George and Daisy, an elderly couple from the Horticultural Society. Cynthia gave them an earful for being late. They ignored her and asked for the washroom. She could hardly refuse. It was part of the agreement to make provision for the volunteers. Besides, they were not your typical retired couple. Daisy had the appearance of someone who'd leave claw marks in the sidewalk of life as time dragged her along. With blue hair, and her 150lbs shrink-wrapped in flamingo pink spandex, she could have been mistaken for one of the people of uncertain means found hanging out downtown. George, her minder, was a grouchy old guy. Friendly as a pitbull with a migraine and fiercely protective of Daisy, as if she'd pulled a splinter out of his paw once. He sat himself down and snapped open a six-pack; one of three he'd brought with him. I could see he was about as stable as—well—as a Pitbull with a migraine. While Cynthia was getting them settled at a card table to take tickets, half the crowd decided to take advantage of the washroom, and while she was trying to keep them out of the house others were sneaking by into the back yard.

Eventually, she got things under control. She locked and bolted the door to the house, and from then on a continuous flow of happy customers passed through the gate to peruse the garden. They oohed and aahed, and sniffed and snorted as they admired the flowers and landscaping. The yard did look gorgeous, and deserved to be featured in 'Landscaper's Digest', but of course I would never tell Cynthia that. Meanwhile, she beamed with pride as she patiently answered questions. That is, at first she was patient. You see, she seemed to be getting the same three or four questions all the time.

"What is that beautiful pink shrub blooming near the front door?" they kept asking.

"It's a Beauty Bush," Cynthia would reply.

"No, what's it called?"

"That is its name—Beauty Bush—really."

By three o'clock she was gritting her teeth as she answered. By three thirty she was ignoring the question. I was watching all this from my deck when she spotted me.

"Ok, Riley," she called out. "All is forgiven. Get over here and help out will you. I need a break."

"Am I still a little creep?"

"No, you're not a little creep." I could swear she emphasised little. I ignored it.

I went around to the front yard where I had to push my way through the line, only to find Gneville taking tickets with Daisy.

"Hi, Mr. Riley. Ticket please."

"I don't have a ticket. I'm coming to help Cynthia. And where's George?"

"He's in the washroom, *again*." Daisy said. "Then he has to mix up some more lemonade. If you don't have a ticket it'll be fifteen dollars please."

"I told you I'm not paying—Hey, I thought the price was ten dollars."

"Lemonade's included," Gneville said. "Isn't that right, Miss Daisy."

"Sure is, Gneville. Charity or not, we aren't sitting out in this hot sun all day for nothing. Every little helps, me being a senior and all. 'Specially since they raised the rent at 'Happy Days.'"

"Did you say 'Happy Days'? I asked.

"Yeah, you got a problem with that?"

"No, not at all," I replied, rolling my eyes as I shouldered my way toward the gate. I received some snide comments on the way, and survived a few nasty digs from the crowd, only to be met by George.

"Stop that one," Daisy yelled, "and make him pay."

It wasn't so much the menacing appearance of George that caused me to turn and retreat; it was more the ambiguity in Daisy's command.

I pushed my way back down the line and returned to the safety of my deck, from where I called down to Cynthia and explained the problem.

"I'll fix those pirates," she said. "You get over here, Riley."

"No way. I'm not running that gauntlet again."

"Come through the fence then. Some of the boards are still loose. I didn't quite finish nailing the new ones up. There's a couple missing still."

"*Cynthia!*"

"*Please,* Riley. I'll bake you a pie or something."

"Large rhubarb with fresh cream?"

"Anything! Just get over here."

I went down the path and found a big hole in the fence behind the spruce tree. "Couple of boards missing," I snorted, "more like four or five." I was able to walk through easily, emerging behind Cynthia's shed. The yard by this time was packed. I could hear a heated discussion going on between Cynthia, George, and

Daisy. It sounded as though Cynthia had met her match. She was backing up as George and Daisy were advancing into the yard. With nobody on the gate the rest of the garden tourists were following like sheep. Cynthia found me and clung to my arm as I tried to fade into the shrubbery.

"What the heck did you say to them, Cynthia? They look awfully angry."

"Nothing really. I just mentioned this was supposed to be for charity, not an unreported pension supplement the taxman might like to hear about."

"Tactful, really tactful. Did you know they were from the 'Happy Days' retirement home."

"They're what? Oh no."

"Take advantage of seniors will you," snarled the approaching Daisy. "Make 'em pay, George." There was no ambiguity in her voice this time. Talk about raging grannies. These two were more like some kind of superannuated terrorist cell out to wreak revenge on suburban boomers.

I was worried. George must have finished the six-pack, and it probably hadn't helped the migraine. He took a step toward us bellowing a stream of abuse.

"You dirty rats, you slimy jackals. Threaten my Daisy would you, you stinking skunks. You skunks?" As he said skunk for the third time George suddenly reversed direction. I looked where his outstretched finger was pointing—to my right, just beneath the shed—a flash of black and white. Cynthia and I froze.

"Remember that funny smell, Cynthia? when we cleaned out the compost? I think I recognize it now." The skunk advanced on George. He turned in retreat, only to find the exit blocked by a crowd of garden tourers. They were sniffing the air like startled antelope.

"Quick," I gasped, "back through the fence."

We made it just in time as George and the skunk squared off. Nevertheless, the whole charity garden tour wasn't sticking around to watch a lopsided contest. They panicked. Around and around the yard they raced. The trampled flowerbeds, knocked over planters, even toppled Manfred. Poor old Daisy fell into a bed of red Salvia which clashed terribly with her pink spandex. What a sight. Some of the more athletic ones leapt the fence like antelopes, while the rest milled around until one of them spotted the hole in the fence. Talk about Wild Kingdom at the waterhole. They charged, straight for the pond. Yes, just like a herd of parched water buffalo, *splash, splash, splash.* Patio pots exploded. Delphiniums devastated. Disaster.

The sun was going down before Cynthia and I felt it safe enough to leave the shed. The scene was terrible. It looked like clear-cutters had been at work.

Cynthia had a strange fluctuating expression on her face as she turned toward me—and a pair of pruning shears in her hand. I sidled toward the sanctity of my shed—too slowly. She launched herself at me, grabbing me in her arms.

This is the end, I thought. Then I realized I wasn't in danger. On the contrary. She was sobbing, great big heaving sobs.

"There there," was the only thing I could think of to comfort her, "it's okay."

"Oh, Riley. What a mess. I'm so sorry. Look what they did to your yard."

"You're sorry," I said, as sympathetically as possible, "wait till you see what they did to *your* yard. They did more than wear the corners off Edgar's pathways."

She sobbed harder. I took her by the arm.

"Come on, Cynthia. Let's go sit on my deck. I think there may be a couple of beers left. We can take stock of things tomorrow."

NO MEANS NO

There is no ancient gentlemen but gardeners...
they hold up Adam's profession.

— Shakespeare

The morning after the garden tour I glanced through the window to see Cynthia hard at work cleaning up the mess in her yard. I went out onto the deck to ask if I could help. She was bent over cursing at a plant she was trying to uproot. I heard her grunt, then she let out a stream of abuse ending in 'Riley'. Oh dear, I thought, now what have I done.

The previous evening we'd sat on the deck for a couple of hours drinking beer, then I found some wine to help marinate our misery. It turned into a party. We had a great time, even ordered a pizza. We told jokes, philosophised, solved most of the world's problems.

We chatted more in that couple of hours than we had in all the time we'd known each other, only to learn we had far more in common than either of us realized. Who'd have believed we were both Wayne Newton fans, loved sauerkraut, and hated blue water flushes?

We even agreed on the best toppings for pizza. When we said goodnight I offered to walk her home. She thanked me but said it wasn't necessary, then surprised me by leaning over to give me a peck on the cheek. At least I thought that's what she had in mind, except I tripped over a chair and almost fell off the deck. She must have thought I was dodging her kiss because she went off in a huff. Now, judging by the sound of it, she probably had a hangover as well and was blaming me. Just when we were getting along so well.

In a gesture of goodwill I decided to make a pot of coffee and take it over to her. I walked down the yard and ducked through the hole in the fence. I was about to say *hi*, when she swore again, louder. Definitely not a time to approach, especially from behind. I backed up quietly, retreating to my yard. Forget it, I thought. Why bother?

I had plenty to do, but I wasn't in any hurry. I took my time finishing my coffee then spent the rest of the morning puttering around the yard. I always find garden work relaxing whatever I'm doing. Not so with Cynthia. I could hear her grumbling as she worked, occasionally mentioning my name. She really had it in for me.

At lunchtime I made a sandwich and sat out in the sun to eat, but I couldn't enjoy it, not with her cursing away. Finally, I'd had enough. I went over to give her a piece of my mind. I found her still heaving on the same plant, a chunk of lavender.

"All right," I yelled, "what exactly is your problem, lady?" I must have startled her. She let out a scream that pierced my ears, blasted through the fence, and blistered the paint on the Hamson's shed. "If you're having so much trouble getting that thing out; why didn't you call for help?"

"I did you bloody idiot. I've been calling all morning. Didn't you hear me?"

"All I heard was cursing. Anyway, I'm here now, so let me help pull it out."

"I don't want the bloody plant out. I'm holding it so that I don't fall over. Oooh, ooh. The only thing that's out is my back. I can't straighten up. Owww, and I'm getting cold."

"Hold on. I mean stay there. I'll go call for help."

I ran to the house, grabbed my cell phone and a blanket, then rushed back.

"Here, this old horse blanket should keep you warm. I've brought a couple of shovels as well, to prop you up 'til help arrives."

"Sounds more like a prelude to shooting me. Who you gonna call, a vet?"

"Don't be silly, I'm going to call 911 for an ambulance."

I punched in the number and waited—nothing.

"O-oh, no wonder."

"Now what?"

"Sorry, Cynthia. I tore out of the house so fast I mistook the TV remote for the phone. I bet the Hamsons are wondering why their TV is acting up. I'll go use the phone in the house. Would you like me to bring you a coffee while I'm there?"

"Jeez, Riley, don't be stupid. I feel bad enough without having to pee too. Hurry up, for Chrisesake, I'm in agony."

"Would you like an aspirin?"

"Move it!"

I raced back to the house again, used the phone, and then dashed back to Cynthia. She was still bent double. I tried not to stare.

"Bad news," I sighed, "I called 911 and got their stupid voice mail. It's impossible to speak to a hot bod...I mean a warm body—I mean..."

"That had better not be a Freudian slip, Riley."

"You know very well what I mean. Anyhow, the message said, "*Because of cutbacks in funding the ambulance is only available on even number days.*" Today's the 9th, so you'll be here 'til tomorrow if we don't find a way to get you out of here." Another stream of curses.

"Wow, you really did spend a lot of time hanging around locker rooms. Some of those words are new to me. Do you think you could try to walk a little?

"I can't even *move*, Riley. If I could I'd slug you.

Ugh! Get it off! Get it off!" I whipped off the blanket.

"Not the blanket you fool."

"Get what off?"

"Something's crawling up the back of my leg. It feels like someone's groping me—*Riley?*"

"It's only a snail. There, it's off. Hey, what do you mean by *groping* you? This is no time for fantasizing, Cynthia. Anyway, I wouldn't dream of it. I'm a perfect gentleman."

"Sure, I can feel you leering."

"I am not leering. I was... Never mind, I've got an idea. Wait here."

"Wait here? Wait here? I've been waiting all morning. Do something."

I explained my plan.

"No way."

"But it's the only way. If you stay out here all night there'll be more than snails crawling over you. I don't need to remind you that you're in a very compromising position."

"A gentleman wouldn't have noticed—Yeoww! Ooh it hurts. All right, go ahead then, but it'd better be painless."

I went back to my yard once more, returning with the wheelbarrow and some cushions.

"Trust me, Cynthia. It'll work."

"Do I have a choice?"

I placed the cushions carefully in the wheelbarrow, fastened them with duct tape, and then stood it on end behind her.

"Okay, let go of the lavender, then ease back into the wheelbarrow. It might hurt a bit, but you'll feel better when you're sitting."

"I can't. I can't let go. My fingers are locked they've been gripping so hard. Oooh, ooh, ow!"

"Well you have to, so here goes."

The manoeuvre went as smoothly as a ship launching. I loosened the lavender with a shovel, then gave Cynthia a little tug. The plant came out by the roots and she rolled slowly backwards. As I lowered the wheelbarrow she sank gently into the cushions—screaming in protest.

"Perfect. Now at least you can look at the sky instead of the ground."

"Thanks. It looks like rain."

"Then we'd better get moving. Do you think you could let go of that plant, or do I have to get the secateurs and cut your fingers off?"

"I'm not in the mood for your sick humour, Riley. Just get me out of here."

I managed to wrench the lavender out of her hand, before pushing her up the path to the house. She was moaning and groaning as the wheelbarrow bounced along. When I went down the step onto the driveway she really screamed.

"I'll kill you for this, Riley."

"Okay, that's it. You're not being fair. I know your back hurts, but I'm only trying to help."

"I'm sorry, Riley, you're right. I shouldn't take it out on you, even if you did reject me last night."

"Reject you? I didn't reject you, I fell over a chair."

"Oh—you did?"

"Yes, you left without even checking to see if I'd hurt myself."

"Well I felt hurt too, and I'm really hurting now."

"So get into the truck."

"Get into the truck? I can't get out of the wheelbarrow."

"*Cynthia*, I can't lift you in. Wait a minute, I've a better idea. Why don't I wheel you down to the plaza? It's all downhill and there's a chiropractor there."

"No way."

"But I told you I can't get you into the truck."

"I said *no way*. No means no. Ooh—ooooh, jeez it hurts. Oh all right, but at least pull the blanket over my head. I don't want the neighbours seeing me."

We set out for the plaza. As I passed the Hamsons, Mr. Hamson was putting the garbage out.

"Hey," he cried, "if you're going to the dump you may as well take this too." He tossed a bag of garbage on top of Cynthia. It would have been funny if not for the extra weight.

"What was that?" she asked.

"Relax, you don't want to know."

I've walked to the plaza many times, and pushed a lot of wheelbarrows, but Cynthia was a challenge. Her weight wasn't distributed very well, the wheel squeaked like crazy, and she whimpered and whined every time I went over a pebble.

"Talk about the Princess and the Pea. Cynthia, this is ridiculous. Do I have to gag you? People are staring. They'll think I'm kidnapping you. Keep it up and you'll have us exposed on the front page of some tabloid—*man caught disposing of alien in garbage*. Buying groceries will be traumatic."

"Ow, ow, just shut up and walk faster."

It may have been downhill but it was farther than I'd realized. By the time we reached the Chiropractor's office my arms had grown six inches and it felt like someone was playing Frisbee with the discs in my back. I shoved Cynthia into the waiting room and collapsed between the shafts of the wheelbarrow.

"Ha! What's this?" the Chiropractor said. "Another garden tour victim I bet. I've had a heck of a day today I can tell you. At least you smell of lavender. I could swear the old guy I had in this morning had tangled with a skunk."

He then turned to me and said, "Okay, wheel her into the examining room and help me get her on the table, then you'd better wait outside. It might get kinda noisy."

I sat in the waiting room listening to the chiropractor work on Cynthia. It sounded much like a goat being strangled. They swore at each other for a while—then silence. He stuck his head out of the door, his brow dripping sweat.

"Boy," he said, "she was a tough one. You can take her home now, but she'll have to rest up for a couple of weeks. And you'd better call a cab. I don't think she wants to ride home in the wheelbarrow."

"Thanks. Come on, Cynthia. The way my back feels you ought to be pushing me home."

When we arrived home I helped her out of the cab and into the house. She'd recovered enough to start fretting about the yard again.

"How the heck can I rest up when the yard is in the state it's in?"

"Don't worry about the yard; I'll take care of it. Just tell me what to do—like you usually do."

"You will? Oh Riley, thank you, that's a weight off my mind. It's times like this I appreciate having you around. You can start by ripping out what's left of the salvia; Daisy must have been rolling in it. But first, please stand Manfred up, he looks like he's dead."

"He is dead. He's a garden gnome, remember? Now, would you like a cup of tea? I know I could use one. I'll get you the TV remote too, and the phone so you can order in. What more could you want? You don't have to leave the couch. It's no wonder they're closing hospitals."

"Riley, you may have the bedside manner of Dr. Strangelove, but thank you, you've been wonderful, and I really appreciate it. I'll make it up to you somehow."

"Sounds like a threat. I can hardly wait."

The next day I finished tidying up my yard and set to work on Cynthia's. Although it was in far worse shape than mine, there really hadn't been any serious damage, other than to Manfred; his ear had come off again. As I worked away I took the opportunity to give her quince a good pruning. I'd been wanting to do it for a long time because of the shade it cast on my roses.

By the end of the first week Cynthia was feeling well enough to get out in the yard again. She didn't say anything about the quince, just frowned at it. The fact is I'd never seen her so relaxed and content. The enforced rest had worked wonders.

She surprised me one morning with coffee and snacks, something I'd been providing her with. I'd even taken supper over once or twice and shocked her with my cooking skills. TV dinners have come a long way.

"Why, thank you," I said, putting down the rake as she handed me a cofffee. "I'm ready for a break. You must be feeling better." "I am. And I can't thank *you* enough, Riley. You've done wonders. You know how I promised I'd make it up to you? Well, I have a gift for you."

"A gift? You don't have to do that. No one buys me gifts. I enjoyed working in your yard. All the clipping and pruning; it's been my pleasure."

"I noticed. Anyway, come along, it's around front. They just delivered it."

We went to see. In the middle of my driveway was an object with a plastic cover over it. I couldn't imagine what it concealed.

"What is it, Cynthia? It looks big enough to be a cultivator, or a leaf shredder. I've always wanted a leaf shredder."

"Close your eyes. I want to do this properly." I was so excited I did as I was told.

I heard rustling, then Cynthia said, "Okay, open them." I opened my eyes, then closed them and tried again. No, it was still there. *It*, was a three-foot high concrete garden gnome in kindergarten colours—female if you can believe it! I felt as thrilled as when I received the letter telling me I'd won fourteen million dollars. The one addressed to occupant.

I had the smile of a ventriloquist's dummy on my face, the words coming automatically, "Thank you, Cynthia. Just what I've always wanted. It's perfect."

"Oh, Riley, I'm so glad you like it. Now we have a matching pair, a symbol of our friendship. Where are you going to put it?"

“I know *exactly* where I'd like to put it.” (But I didn't tell her).

“I'm going to leave it right here out front, right where all the world can see.” (And right where I could load it into my truck and take it to the dump). Symbol or no symbol it had to go. I'd already begun formulating a plan to have it 'stolen'.

That night before retiring I left my truck beside the monstrosity. I set my alarm and at three I woke up and got dressed. I went outside hoping the thing might have been stolen already. Not a chance. I quietly lowered the tailgate then bent over to lift the gnome into the truck. It was heavy—too heavy. I screamed silently as my back surrendered. I crumpled to my knees, unable to move. I cursed and cursed, mostly Cynthia, and under my breath. Despite the pain I couldn't let her find out I'd been up to anything.

At dawn I was still in the same position, my arms locked around the gnome. When old Hamson left for work he hollered across the street, “Hey Riley, a simple good morning will suffice. What you're doing could get you arrested.” I gave a weak smile that I'm sure looked more like a leer.

At seven o'clock Stay showed up. For a stupid dog he clearly recognized the opportunity to explore the concept of retribution. I crouched there with wet feet until eight thirty when Cynthia discovered me. She burst into laughter.

"Oh, Riley, that's so sweet. I wasn't really sure you liked your gift, and here you are hugging her. Let me get my camera."

"Aaaaaaaaaaaarg. Forget the frigging camera. I've put my back out."

"You have? Oh, no, you can't have, Riley. I had a special evening planned for us. I was going to invite you for dinner, and *really* show my thanks."

"You were? Cynthia? What do you mean by, *really* show your thanks?"

"*Riley.* You know…"

"Wait a minute, it's not so bad. I think I might be able to stand up. Ooh, ooh, aaaargh—yeeow. It's no good, I can't move. You'd better call an ambulance."

"You're right. You do look a little pale, and your eyes are watering. I'll call them right away. Wait a minute, what's the date?"

"The 23rd."

"Oh dear, we're not going to have much luck with warm bodies today, are we, Riley?"

"Fetch the wheelbarrow, Cynthia."

What a man needs in gardening
is a cast iron back with a hinge in it.

THE END?
—You've got to be kidding…

ORDER FORM

For copies of **Soiled Reputations**

Send cheque or money order to:

Flip Publishing
162 Herron Pl.
Waterloo, Ontario, Canada
N2T 1H2
dhobson@golden.net
www.golden.net/~dhobson

Quantity ______ x Price _____ + Shipping 3.00

TOTAL_____

Canadian price: $15.95
U.S. price: $13.95

Deliver to:

Name ________________________________

Address ________________________________

City __________________ Prov./State __________

Code __________________ Country ___________

- Make cheques payable to *David Hobson*
- Allow 4-6 weeks delivery